WATER, CHEMISTRY & ECOLOGY

The Book Society of Canada Limited, Agincourt, Canada
John Murray, London

JOE HAMMILL

The Book Society of Canada Limited   ISBN 0-7725-2006-2
John Murray ISBN 0-7195-3689-8

THE ACTION CHEMISTRY SERIES

Core book
Action Chemistry Ken Ashcroft

Modules
Chemistry of Man & Molecules Lou Birenbaum
Chemistry of Photography Ken Ashcroft
Chemistry of the Car Ken Ashcroft and Joe Hammill
Water, Chemistry & Ecology Joe Hammill
Chemistry of Metallurgy Graham Worthington

Further titles are under consideration.

Design Brant Cowie

Artwork Frank Zsigo

Canadian Calaloguing in Publication Data

Hammill, Joe, 1941-
    Water, chemistry & ecology

(The Action chemistry series)

Bibliography: p.
Includes index.
ISBN 0-7725-2006-2

1. Water - Composition - Experiments. 2. Water - Pollution - Experiments. I. Title. II. Series.

QD169.W3H35 1979   546'.22   C79-094413-8

Printed in Canada

2 3 4 5 6 7 8 BP 85 84 83 82 81 80 79

The Book Society of Canada Limited, Agincourt, Canada, M1S 3B6
John Murray (Publishers) Ltd., 50 Albemarle Street, London W1X 4BD, U.K.

Contents

Acknowledgments

Permission to reproduce illustrations is gratefully acknowledged below. Care has been taken in the preparation of these acknowledgments; the publisher would appreciate being informed of any errors.

K. Ashcroft Cover, 6-2, 6-3
Atomic Energy of Canada 4-1, 4-2
E. Lyon Barnum 3-8
Culligan of Canada Ltd. 2-2, 2-7, 2-8
Federal Ministry of Transport 4-3
Heinemann Educational Books
  (*Chemistry Takes Shape, Book 4*
   A.H. Johnstone and T.I. Morrison) 2-5
Israel Information Service, New York 5-6

Miller Services 2-6, page 12
Millipore Ltd. 3-16
Ontario Ministry of the Environment
  Title page, 3-13, 3-14, 3-15, 3-18, page 28,
  4-4, 5-3, 7-1
Ontario Science Centre 3-6, 3-10
The Permutit Company of Canada, Inc.
  2-1, 5-1, 5-2
Unilever Limited 6-4, 6-5

Author's acknowledgments

I would like to acknowledge the help provided by the science staff of Barton Secondary School, Hamilton, Ontario; namely, Ted Ayliffe, Joyce Leslie, Gord Stevens, Don Johnson, and Audrey Gleave. They saved me many trips to the encyclopaedia.

I wish to thank Ken Ashcroft for much help and inspiration during the writing of this book, and also Linda Zajac, who typed the manuscript so expertly from my handwriting.

Joe Hammill, July 1974

To the teacher

This booklet is an introduction to the study of the vital role that water plays in life on this planet. For centuries water has been regarded as a limitless and forgiving receptacle for all the wastes of mankind. Now the realization is dawning that this is not so. Water must be treated with respect or else we will suffer for it.

The emphasis in this booklet, then, is on the ecological implications of the abuse of water. First, natural water is studied. In later chapters, particular forms of water pollution are considered. Always the emphasis is on understanding, growing from the experiments; no fewer than thirty-five experiments are included. It is hoped that this experimental approach, rather than long theoretical discussions, will help to make the implications of water pollution more real to students.

It is expected that students using this booklet will already have a basic understanding of chemistry.

In this series, as revised, only SI units and those derived from or compatible with SI have been used. A table and definitions of these are provided on pages 56 and 57. In keeping with the attempt to discourage students from converting SI units to those they replace, the latter have been given their SI equivalents, rather than *vice versa*. This should be of positive value in the event that the student is called upon to consult old notes or older texts. The values have been given as accurately as the data and a twelve-digit calculator would permit, so that rounding-off can be performed to the degree of accuracy desired.

While the point (.) has been used as the decimal marker, it should be made clear that the comma (,) is used for this purpose extensively throughout the world — and more immediately in French-language texts in Canada.

The cubic decimetre (dm^3) has been used instead of the litre (L) in all lab work and references, while the litre has been retained when referring to domestic and industrial quantities and use. The kelvin (K) has been used *only* when referring to units of the absolute temperature *scale*; actual temperatures are stated in degrees Celsius ($^{\circ}C$). In molar concentrations, the unit $mol\cdot dm^{-3}$ has replaced the symbol M. In addition, every effort within reason has been made to conform to the IUPAC system of nomenclature and spelling.

The raised dot ($\cdot$) as multiplication sign in conjunction with negative superscript numerals ($^{-1}$) has been used in compound units instead of the solidus (/) to signify 'per' or division (e.g. $3\ g\cdot dm^{-3}$). While this convention may be unfamiliar to some students, they will be increasingly exposed to it in coming years. A few moments practice reading aloud such terms correctly should overcome any initial difficulty.

Figure 1-1. Some of the many uses of water. Included are hyperbolic cooling towers and a water turbine.

1

Water in your life

"Even the Archbishop of Canterbury is 65 per cent water."

J.B.S. Haldane

World's water supplies

Water? Why bother to study water? Water is such an ordinary common substance. Most of us take it for granted. But think for a couple of minutes of some of the uses of water. Suggest additional examples to those shown in Figure 1-1.

Now make a list of things that can be done or made *without* water. Can you think of many? Can you think of *any*? Water is essential to life. Our bodies are composed of about 65 per cent water. Without water to drink, we would die within a few days.

This book will help you to study the chemistry of water and some of the ways in which water is vital. After you have completed the experiments in this book, you should realize why water must be treated with respect. Abuse it, and eventually you will suffer.

Between two-thirds and three-quarters of the surface of the Earth is covered by water. The world's total supply of water in all three states (liquid, solid and vapour), on the surface, underground and in the atmosphere, amounts to 1 359 000 000 cubic kilometres (liquid measure). Of this total, however, 1 320 000 000 km^3 are salty. A further 29 000 000 km^3 are 'locked up' in the polar ice caps, glaciers and permanent snowfields; and 5 900 000 km^3 are trapped deep in the Earth's crust. This leaves less than one-third of one per cent (0.3%) as fresh water in circulation. (See hydrologic cycle, page 2.)

About 6 000 litres (cubic decimetres) of fresh water are used per day in North America for each of the 245 million Canadians and Americans. There are 10^{12} dm^3 in 1 km^3. What percentage of the world's available fresh water is used in Canada and the U.S. each day?

Figure 1-2 The distribution of water on the planet Earth.

One two-hundred-thousandth (0.0005%) of the world's available fresh water easily sustains the earth's population.

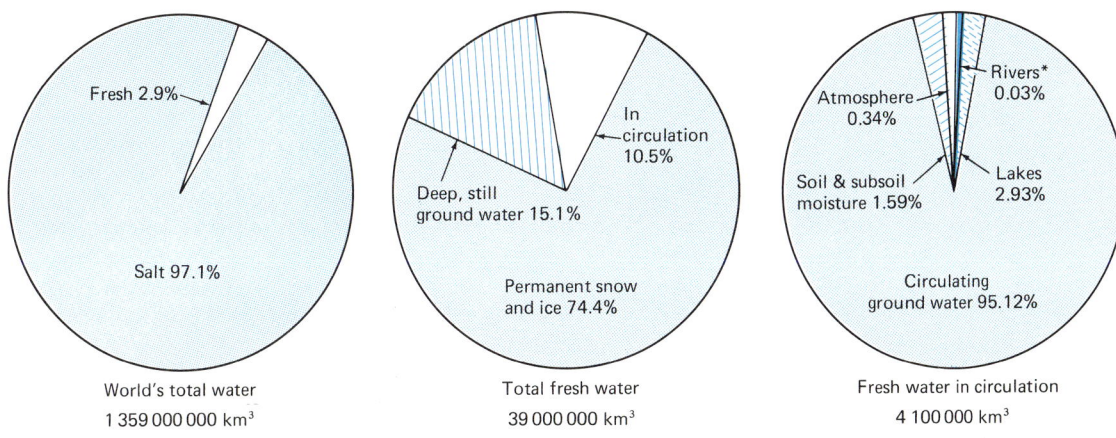

World's total water
1 359 000 000 km³

Total fresh water
39 000 000 km³

Fresh water in circulation
4 100 000 km³

* Rivers include runoff from the Arctic, the Antarctic and small oceanic islands.

N.B. When calculating with these figures, round off your results to the nearest thousand or ten thousand — as the case may be — except with rivers (1 200 km³) and the large quantities already given. Note that the total ground water, both still and slowly circulating, is by far the largest *liquid* fresh-water resource.

On a hot day a good-sized apple tree may lose, or transpire, 5 litres (dm^3) of water per minute.

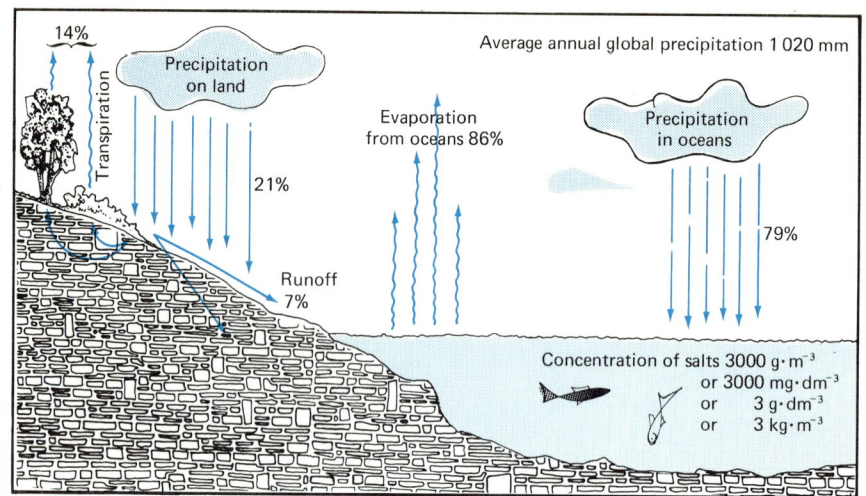

Figure 1-3. The hydrologic cycle. All evaporated water is pure.

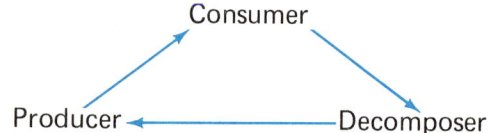

Consumer

Producer ← Decomposer

Ecology

The main causes of the daily gains and losses of water in the human body are:

Gains	cm^3
Drink	1300
Food	850
Food oxidation	350
	2500

Losses	cm^3
Evaporation from lungs	400
Evaporation from skin	500
Water in urine	1500
Water in faeces	100
	2500

If the fresh water we use were not replaced as fresh water, then obviously the total supply would soon diminish. Fortunately nature has its own purifying system called the hydrologic cycle. (Figure 1-3.)

Water is vital to humans, but humanity is not the only form of life on this earth that needs it. Other creatures and plants use water either directly or indirectly. Many are born, live and die in water. Humans must share the world's water with other living things.

What can happen if humans are too greedy? To understand some of the implications behind this question, you should know a little about ecology and cycles in nature.

We are *consumers*, and some of our body wastes are poisonous to us. If we breathe in too much carbon dioxide we will suffocate. If we eat our own faeces we will be poisoned. These products must be *decomposed* or changed. Among the decomposers are bacteria and fungi. They break down our waste products into simpler forms, such as nitrates, carbon dioxide, and urea.

The main *producers* are plants. They turn our decomposed waste products (carbon dioxide, nitrates, minerals, and so on) into substances we consume: oxygen, carbohydrate foods, and proteins. This is done by the process of photosynthesis. And so the cycle goes on. . . .

How is all this related to water? Fish are consumers, bacteria are decomposers, and plants are producers as before. Bacteria decompose the waste products from water life, but when we dump our wastes into the same water, then the equilibrium is upset. For example, you have probably read reports that Lake Erie is 'dying' because of all the human, industrial and domestic wastes in it. What has happened is that man, either through ignorance or choice, has overloaded a natural ecosystem. We say that the lake is polluted.

Do the ecologies of humans and fish, or earth and water, interrelate? Humans obtain food from the rivers, lakes and oceans by fishing. Water dissolves most of the carbon dioxide from excretion and decomposition; green water-plants, mostly algae and other phytoplankton, use this dissolved carbon dioxide in photosynthesis, and produce oxygen in the process. The excess oxygen replenishes the atmosphere. Water, as we have noted, is also a major and important part of the human body.

Age of the Earth

One interesting application of the hydrologic cycle has been in helping to estimate the age of the earth. It is assumed that the seas originally contained fresh water, and the salts that are now in the sea have flowed into it from the river runoff. If the rate of this flow has remained constant, then the time taken for the seas to arrive at their present salt concentrations can be calculated. According to these calculations, the age of the oceans is about five billion years. This is in rough agreement with calculations based on the potassium-argon and uranium-lead methods of dating rocks.

Where did we come from?

Theories have been propounded that life started in the oceans and that man has ultimately evolved from sea life. One of the facts that favour these theories is that most animal species, including humans, require a constant internal environment, that is, a constant body temperature. These species have to learn to adapt to great changes in the external environment. The oceans with their large mass of water would have minimised any changes in the external environment and hence made it easier for animal species to survive.

An intriguing piece of evidence has been produced from the study of the concentrations of salts in the blood of sea animals and land animals. These tend to be about the same, and almost equivalent to the concentration of salts in the ocean.

In spite of the evidence that supports them, however, these notions are still highly theoretical.

Some interesting observations on fresh water resources

The atmosphere contains 10 times as much water as all the rivers on Earth.

Rock and soil contain 73 times as much water as all the Earth's rivers, lakes and atmosphere, combined.

There is 215 times as much water in permanent snow and ice as in all other fresh water above ground.

In the next four chapters we shall discuss how nature's ecological balance is being upset by man's pollutants.

2

Domestic water

Figure 2-1. Photograph of a pipe through which water once flowed. The scale built up over a period of time.

Hardness in water

Water . . . is water . . . is water. Or is it? Take a look at Figure 2-1. Why is the water-pipe clogged? The pipe is made of copper, which is not soluble in water, so presumably something in the water must have caused the substance to form. In investigating why the pipe became almost useless, you will learn about *permanently hard* water, *temporarily hard* water, and *soft* water, and how problems created by widely differing kinds of water are solved.

Experiment 2.1
Preparation of hard water

Take 3 samples of distilled water in separate beakers. To sample 1 add a few cubic centimetres of calcium hydroxide solution. Stir well. Insert a glass tube into the beaker and blow carefully through the tube until the contents turn cloudier and then clearer. Filter the contents into a clean beaker and keep the filtrate.

To sample 2 add a few grams of calcium sulfate, stir well and then filter. Keep the filtrate.

Do not add anything to sample 3. You now have three test samples.

Experiment 2.2
Effect of soap on hard water

Pour a sample of liquid from each beaker into clean test tubes, and add 5 drops of soap solution to each tube. Shake well and record how much lather each sample produced. Which sample do you think would be the best for washing?

Experiment 2.3
Destruction of temporary hardness

Pour another sample from each beaker into clean test tubes. Boil the samples for about 1 minute. Allow them to cool. Do you notice any changes?

Add 5 drops of soap solution to each test tube and shake well. Compare the lathers in Experiment 2.2 with those just produced. What has happened? If there has been a change, in which test tube did it occur? Suggest a reason.

Figure 2-2. Soap in hard and soft water. Which is which?

Why, then, do some types of water give a good lather while others give hardly any lather at all? Consider Experiment 2.1 and the particles added to the samples of distilled water. In sample 1, first calcium hydroxide was added and then carbon dioxide from your breath. The carbon dioxide combined with the water:

$$\text{carbon dioxide} \ + \text{water} \longrightarrow \text{carbonic acid}$$
$$CO_2 \qquad + \ H_2O \ \longrightarrow \qquad H_2CO_3$$

The carbonic acid reacted with the calcium hydroxide:

$$\text{carbonic acid} \quad + \ \text{calcium hydroxide} \ \longrightarrow \text{calcium carbonate} + \text{water}$$
$$H_2CO_3 \qquad + \qquad Ca(OH)_2 \qquad \longrightarrow \qquad CaCO_3 \qquad + \ 2H_2O$$
$$2H^+_{(aq)} + CO_3{}^{2-}_{(aq)} \ + Ca^{2+}_{(aq)} + 2OH^-_{(aq)} \ \longrightarrow \qquad Ca^{2+}CO_3{}^{2-}_{(aq)} \ + \ 2H_2O$$

The extra white cloudiness you saw was the insoluble precipitate, calcium carbonate. The reaction did not stop at that stage, however. The carbonic acid then reacted with the calcium carbonate:

$$\text{carbonic acid} \quad + \ \text{calcium carbonate} \longrightarrow \text{calcium hydrogen carbonate}$$
$$H_2CO_3 \qquad + \qquad CaCO_3 \qquad \longrightarrow \qquad Ca(HCO_3)_2$$
$$2H^+_{(aq)} + CO_3{}^{2-}_{(aq)} + \qquad Ca^{2+}CO_3{}^{2-}_{(s)} \quad \longrightarrow Ca^{2+}_{(aq)} + 2HCO_3{}^-_{(aq)}$$

The insoluble calcium carbonate changed to soluble calcium hydrogen carbonate, which explains the decreasing cloudiness in sample 1 in Experiment 2.1. When filtered, only the soluble calcium and hydrogen carbonate ions came through the filter paper.

To sample 2 calcium sulfate was added.

$$Ca^{2+}SO_4{}^{2-}_{(s)} \rightleftharpoons Ca^{2+}_{(aq)} + SO_4{}^{2-}_{(aq)}$$

Only the Ca^{2+} ions and $SO_4{}^{2-}$ ions that separated passed through the filter paper. Compared to some solutes, calcium sulfate has a relatively low solubility in water.

What particle do both solutions have in common?

The magnesium ion has exactly the same effect as the calcium ion. Water containing one or both of these ions is called *hard* water. (Figure 2-2.)

How water becomes hard.

We all breathe out carbon dioxide gas; the internal combustion engine exhausts carbon dioxide; aeroplanes produce carbon dioxide, and so on. Therefore the atmosphere must contain carbon dioxide. Carbon dioxide is soluble in water, so that rainwater contains a certain amount of carbonic acid.

Calcium carbonate occurs in several forms. Some of these are chalk, marble, and limestone. Calcium carbonate is also a binding agent in sandstone rocks. Magnesium carbonate occurs as magnesite.

When acidified rainwater runs off these rocks, some of the calcium and magnesium go into solution as free ions. Write the chemical equation for the reaction of carbonic acid with magnesium carbonate.

The daily average use of domestic water per person in Ontario is approximately as follows:

Bath	130 litres
Shower	85 litres
Laundering	85 litres
Rinsing	85 litres
Dish washing	40 litres
Toilet	40 litres

In Experiment 2.3 the hardness of one of the samples was destroyed by boiling. This also caused a white insoluble substance to form.

calcium hydrogen carbonate $\longrightarrow$ calcium carbonate + carbon dioxide + water

$$Ca(HCO_3)_2 \longrightarrow CaCO_3 + CO_2 + H_2O$$
$$Ca^{2+}(aq) + 2HCO_3(aq) \longrightarrow Ca^{2+}CO_3{}^{2-}(s) + CO_2(g) + H_2O(l)$$

This equation shows that the free calcium ions have become bound to carbonate ions. Since they are no longer free, the water is no longer hard. Write the equation for the reaction when magnesium hydrogen carbonate solution is boiled.

Temporarily hard water is the name given to water whose hardness can be destroyed by boiling.

Permanent hardness

We still have to consider *permanent* hardness, the state of the sample whose hardness was not destroyed by boiling. Calcium ions can enter the water supply in a different way from that described above. Gypsum (calcium sulfate dihydrate, $CaSO_4 \cdot 2H_2O$) is slightly soluble in water:

$$Ca^{2+}SO_4{}^{2-}(s) \rightleftharpoons Ca^{2+}(aq) + SO_4{}^{2-}(aq)$$

So again the offending calcium ion can enter the water supply if water flows over rocks containing gypsum. Boiling will have no effect on the hardness of this solution of calcium sulfate.

Water-softening techniques

In removing temporary hardness, use was made of the insolubility of calcium carbonate. Can this property remove permanent hardness?

Experiment 2.4
Removal of
permanent hardness

Make some permanently hard water by dissolving 2 g of magnesium sulfate in $200\ cm^3$ of water. Pour 2 samples into clean test tubes. To the first add 5 drops of soap solution, and shake. Describe what happens.

To the second test tube add a few crystals of sodium carbonate, and shake. Describe what happens. Now add 5 drops of soap solution, and shake. Again, what happens?

The sodium carbonate removed the hardness, and hence must have removed the magnesium ions. Actually the carbonate ions combined with the magnesium ions to form the solid, magnesium carbonate, which was the whiteness visible after you added the sodium carbonate crystals.

That leaky tap – a drip a second means 15 litres (dm^3) of water down the drain in twenty-four hours.

magnesium ions + sodium carbonate $\longrightarrow$ magnesium carbonate + sodium ions

$$Mg^{2+}(aq) + 2Na^{+}(aq) + CO_3{}^{2-}(aq) \longrightarrow Mg^{2+}CO_3{}^{2-}(s) + 2Na^{+}(aq)$$

The sodium ions now free and the solid magnesium carbonate do not make water hard, but they can cause other problems. We shall consider some of these later. Of course, if calcium ions had been present in the water, calcium carbonate would also have been formed.

Ask your mother—or maybe your grandmother—whether she ever used 'washing soda'. Washing soda is the common name for sodium carbonate. This old-fashioned method of softening water has been superseded by a technique using an ion-exchange column.

Experiment 2.5
Action of an
ion-exchange column

Make a concentrated solution of cobalt sulfate crystals in water. The pink colour is a property of the cobalt ion. Pour about 10 cm^3 into a column (a burette) filled with the ion-exchange resin. When about 5 cm^3 of liquid have passed through the column, pour two 10 cm^3 portions of distilled water down the column. Does anything happen? If so, what?

Now pour a concentrated solution of sodium chloride into the column. What happens? What is the colour of the solution emitted at the bottom of the column? What substance or substances would you say are now trapped in the resin? What would you say were the contents of the collector?

Use the evidence from this experiment to explain the working of an ion-exchange resin. (The name should give you a hint.) Does your explanation help you to suggest an answer to the problem of hard water?

Experiment 2.6
Removal of permanent
hardness by ion exchange

Using the same resin from Experiment 2.5, flush the column with the concentrated sodium chloride solution until no more pink-coloured liquid leaves the column.

Pour a sample of permanently hard water into the column and collect the emitted liquid in a clean beaker. Add 5 drops of soap solution to the beaker, and shake it. What is produced? Has the water been softened?

The salt water emitted from the column in this experiment is not hard, but it does contain sodium ions. No precipitated calcium carbonate or magnesium carbonate is contained in this water, but the resin eventually has to be flushed with sodium chloride solution to remove the trapped calcium and/or magnesium ions before re-use.

Besides calcium and magnesium ions, the ions of iron, lead and some other metals also make water hard. Figure 2-3 shows how an ion-exchange column works.

Industry needs vast quantities of steam power and if this is produced from hard water, scaly deposits of carbonates and sulfates will form on the inside surfaces of the boilers. These deposits are the same as the 'fur' often found in kettles. Carbonates and sulfates are pour conductors of heat. This means that much heat energy will be lost, making the steam more expensive to produce. Many modern steam-producing systems use ion-exchange water softeners. The calcium and magnesium chlorides resulting from the flushing process are drained off and join the vast general water supply.

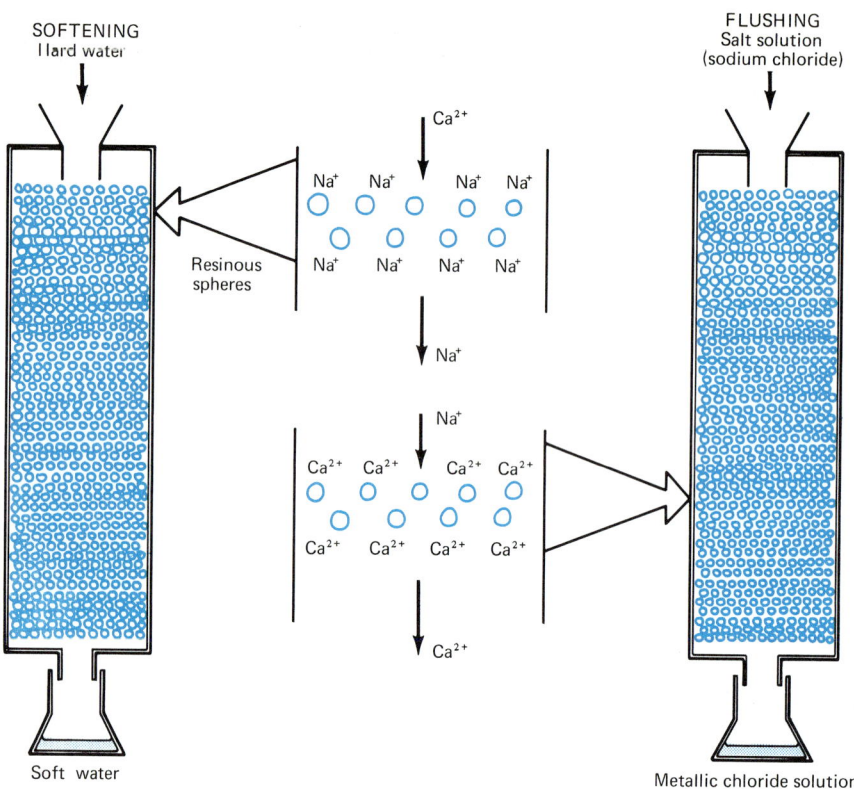

Figure 2-3. How an ion-exchange column works.

Action of soap in hard water

All sodium salts are soluble in water. One type of soap contains a sodium salt called sodium octadecanoate (sodium stearate), which we shall denote as Na^+St^-. The stearate ion is actually $C_{17}H_{35}COO^-$. When free in solution it is the cleaning agent in the soap. If the stearate ion is not free but combines with another substance in the water, the soap will not work well.

$$\text{sodium stearate} + \text{calcium ions} \longrightarrow \text{calcium stearate} + \text{sodium ions}$$
$$2Na^+_{(aq)} + 2St^-_{(aq)} + Ca^{2+}_{(aq)} \longrightarrow Ca^{2+}St_2^-_{(s)} + 2Na^+_{(aq)}$$
and also
$$2Na^+_{(aq)} + 2St^-_{(aq)} + Mg^{2+}_{(aq)} \longrightarrow Mg^{2+}St_2^-_{(s)} + 2Na^+_{(aq)}$$

Thus, in hard water, the stearate ion is no longer free and the soap has little effect. Calcium and magnesium stearate are insoluble compounds; they are the scum that is formed in bath water.

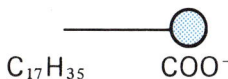

$$C_{17}H_{35} \quad COO^-$$

Figure 2-4 (above). When in solution, a stearate ion has a hydrophobic (water-hating) tail – $C_{17}H_{35}$ – and a hydrophylic (water-loving) head – COO^-. (This is only a diagrammatic representation. The stearate ion does not actually look like this.)

Figure 2-5 (right) Stearate ions freeing grease from a surface. In (b) the water-hating tails stick in the grease. In (c) the negatively-charged heads repel one another and start to break up the grease. In (d) agitation helps to break the grease into smaller particles, and spread them throughout the water. The presence of the negatively-charged stearate ions in the grease particles prevents them from coming together. This type of mixture is called an emulsion.

The stearate ion has a water-loving (hydrophilic) head and a water-hating (hydrophobic) tail. The head is negatively charged.

Consider a piece of greasy cloth placed in soapy soft water. (See Figures 2-4 and 2-5.) The water-hating tails stick in the grease, while the water-loving heads stick out into the water. The heads, being negatively charged, push each other away. The result is that particles of grease are spread throughout the water. This is called an emulsion. The grease particles are freed from the cloth and, with agitation and rinsing, the cloth is cleaned.

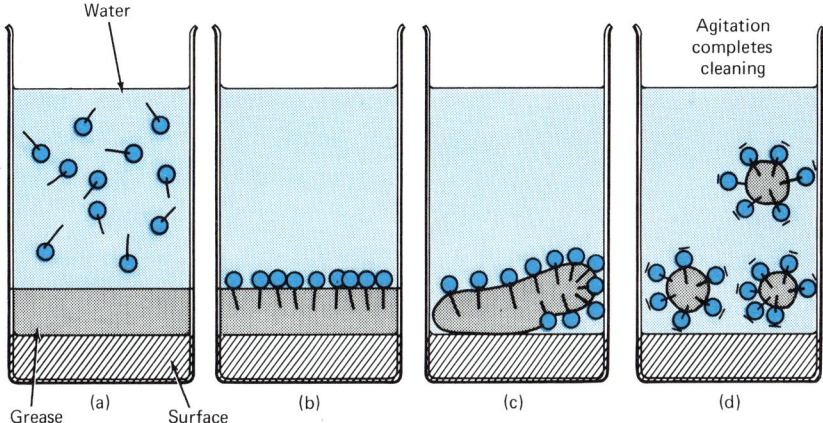

Synthetic detergents — a mixed blessing?

Experiment 2.7
Detergents and water

Another 'answer' to the hard-water problem in the washing and cleaning process came with the discovery of synthetic detergents.

Take a sample of hard water, add 5 drops of detergent, and shake. What do you notice?

There is, therefore, a substance created by chemists that cleans effectively in hard water. In synthetic detergents an ion is used that does not combine with calcium or magnesium ions to form a precipitate or scum.

Although detergents solved one problem — that of hard water — they created another. In replacing the stearate ion, chemists substituted a non-biodegradable ion. This meant that the bacteria in the settling tanks of sewage plants could no longer 'digest' these ions by breaking them down into simpler forms. The result was the accumulation of ugly mounds of foam at some sewage works and at sewage outlets to rivers.

Figure 2-6 (right). The result of using non-biodegradable detergents.

Figure 2-7 (below). These photomicrographs show four strands of hair, two washed in soft water, the other two in hard water. Which are which?

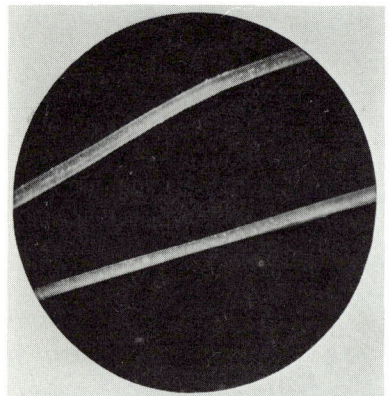

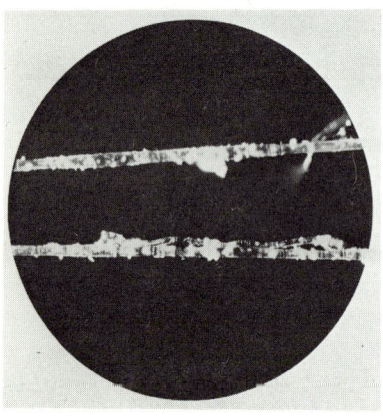

Phosphates in detergents greatly improve their whitening qualities. When phosphates are discharged into rivers, lakes and streams, they tend to encourage the growth of algae. This is called *eutrophication* and is a major pollution problem. For this reason some governments have banned the use of phosphate detergents. Chemists have modified the detergent ion to make it biodegradable and still fairly effective. (See *Action Chemistry*, page 107.) Thus, by a little molecular juggling and a small sacrifice in whitening power, chemists have succeeded in providing us with synthetic detergents that are no longer a major source of pollution.

Total hardness

You can measure the total hardness of a water sample. The result is expressed in parts per million of calcium carbonate. As hardness values are always given in this way, regardless of the source or kind of hardness, samples from widely separated locations can be compared.

Figure 2-8. Which bowl of peas was cooked in hard water and which in soft water?

Experiment 2.8
Estimating total hardness

Take a 50 cm^3 sample of tap water and add 10 cm^3 of buffer solution. (This solution is prepared by mixing 67.5 g of ammonium chloride with 570 cm^3 of concentrated ammonia solution and diluting to 1 dm^3.) Now add to the sample 4 or 5 drops of the indicator Eriochrome Black T. Titrate edta (ethylenediamine-tetraacetic acid) solution into the sample until it changes colour from wine-red to blue. Check on the label that 1 cm^3 of your edta solution corresponds to 1 mg CaCO$_3$.

The number of cubic centimetres of edta solution equals the number of milligrams of calcium carbonate present in the sample of water.

Here is an example. Suppose your sample of tap water required 7.5 cm^3 of edta solution to bring about the required colour change. In 50 cm^3 of tap water, then, there are 7.5 mg of calcium carbonate. In 1000 cm^3 of tap water there are 7.5 × 20 mg of calcium carbonate. Therefore the total hardness of the sample of tap water is 150 mg·dm^{-3} or 150 ppm. Check with your municipal authority to find out whether your local hardness is high or low compared with other parts of Canada.

Summary

Temporarily hard water
Cause: Acidified rainwater flowing over chalk, limestone, dolomite, magnesite, etc. produces the hydrogen carbonates of calcium and magnesium.
Effects: Produces scum with soap, and scale when boiled.
Removed by: Water softener, ion-exchange, boiling.

Permanently hard water
Cause: Rainwater flowing over gypsum, epsomite, etc. dissolves calcium and magnesium ions.
Effects: Produces scum with soap, and scale when boiled. If too hard it is un-drinkable.
Removed by: Water softener, ion-exchange.

3

Water and life cycles

Water and oxygen

Experiment 3.1
Estimating dissolved oxygen

In Chapter 2 you learned about water used in the home. In this chapter you will study water as it is found in rivers, lakes, and other bodies of water.

The most important property of bodies of water is their ability to support life. This ability usually depends directly on the amount of oxygen in the water — that is, the concentration of oxygen gas molecules dissolved in the water, and not the oxygen atoms bonded to hydrogen atoms in the water molecules themselves.

Note: concentrated sulfuric acid is very dangerous. Do not handle this acid without the permission of your teacher.

Collect a water sample in a glass-stoppered bottle, capacity 250 cm^3. Fill the bottle completely. Do not leave an air space at the top.

Add 1 cm^3 of a 3 mol·dm^{-3} solution of manganese(II) sulfate by means of a pipette, dipping the end of the pipette well below the surface of the sample. Add 1 cm^3 of alkaline potassium iodide solution in the same way. Insert the stopper and mix the contents by turning the bottle upside down several times.

Allow the precipitate to settle half-way, then mix the contents again. Let the precipitate settle half-way once more before adding 1 cm^3 of concentrated sulfuric acid. Insert the stopper immediately and mix as before until the precipitate disappears. Allow the solution to stand for 5 minutes.

Withdraw 100 cm^3 of the solution into an Erlenmeyer flask. Immediately add a 0.025 mol·dm^{-3} solution of sodium thiosulfate from a burette until the yellow colour nearly disappears. Add 1 cm^3 of starch solution and continue adding the thiosulfate solution, stopping immediately when the blue colour disappears. Record the amount of thiosulfate solution used. (Disregard any return of the blue colour.)

Double the recorded figure. The result gives the number of parts per million (ppm) of oxygen dissolved in the water (solution).

Instructions for the preparation of solutions for Experiment 3.1:

Manganese(II) sulfate. Dissolve about 480 g of manganese(II) sulfate crystals (MnSO$_4$·4H$_2$O) or 400 g of MnSO$_4$·2H$_2$O in sufficient distilled water to make 1 dm^3 of solution.

Alkaline potassium iodide. Dissolve about 500 g of sodium hydroxide and 150 g of potassium iodide in sufficient distilled water to make 1 dm^3 of solution. This solution is caustic. Take care.

Sodium thiosulfate solution (0.025 mol·dm^{-3}). Dissolve 6.205 g of sodium thiosulfate in 1 dm^3 of distilled water. Na$_2$S$_2$O$_3$·5H$_2$O crystals should be used. If the crystals have turned white, because of loss of water of crystallization (water of hydration), they should not be used.

Starch indicator. Make a thin paste of about 2 g of starch in cold water. Pour it into 200 cm^3 of boiling water and stir. When it is cool, add a few drops of trichloromethane (chloroform).

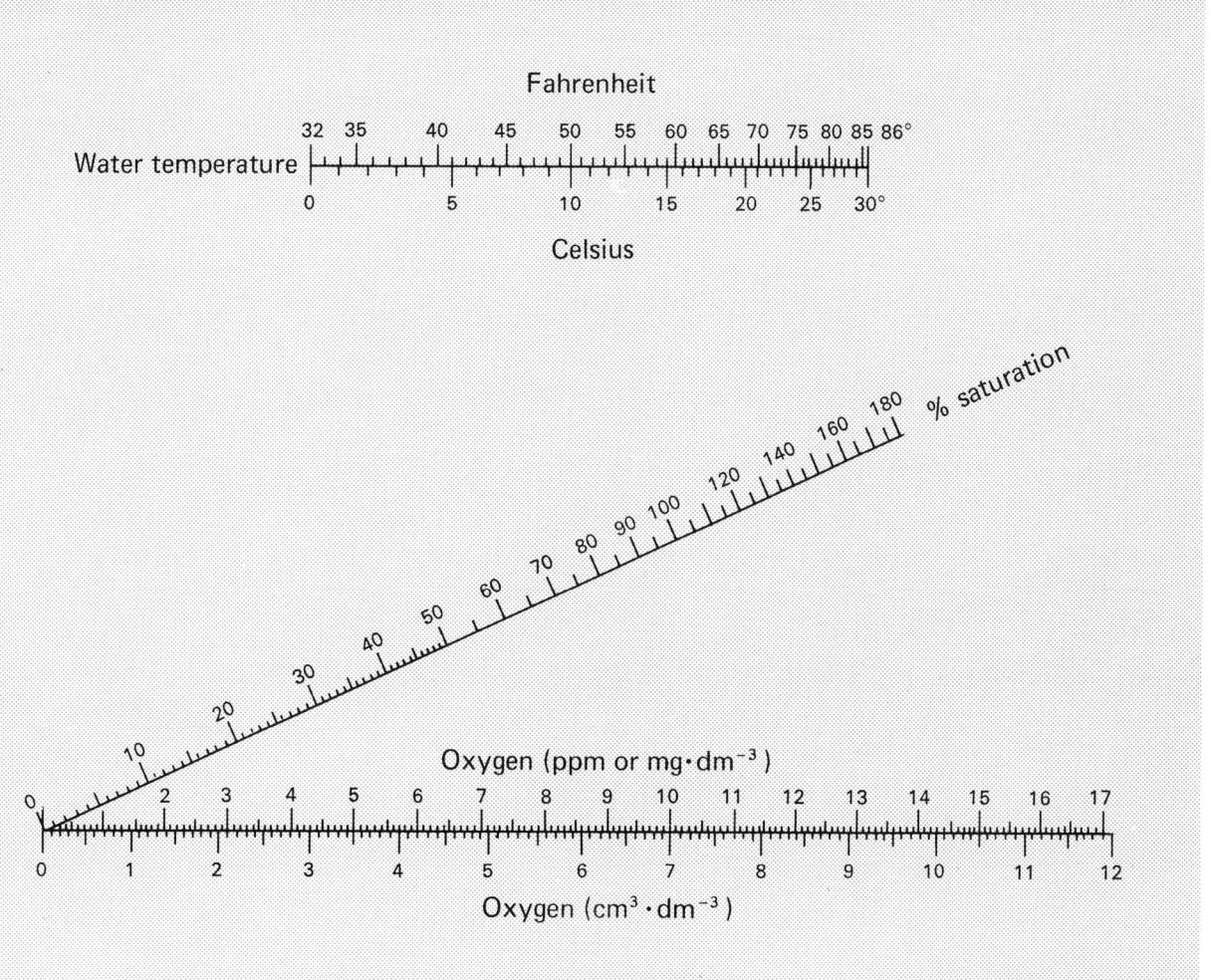

Figure 3-1. Rawson's nomogram. If you know the water temperature and the dissolved oxygen content, you can find the percentage oxygen saturation of a water sample. Suppose your sample of water has a dissolved oxygen content of 4 mg·dm^{-3} or 4 ppm, at 7°C. Join these two points with a ruler and read off the percentage saturation of the water. In this case it is about 32 per cent.

This experiment is called the Winkler method of finding the dissolved oxygen content of any water sample.

Normally water can contain only a certain amount of dissolved oxygen at any given temperature. The maximum concentration is very low — for example at 15°C it is 10 ppm, just 10 mg of oxygen in every litre (dm^3) of water — but the presence of dissolved oxygen in water, even in much lower concentration, is of the utmost importance. Most species that live in water rely on this dissolved oxygen for their life processes.

Different species of fish require particular minimum levels of dissolved oxygen, and if the water does not contain this concentration, the species cannot survive. The fish we eat (particularly trout) are the first to perish when the dissolved oxygen decreases. In North America, the species least susceptible to oxygen depletion is the catfish. (See page 25.)

How oxygen gets into water.

Some of the oxygen dissolved in bodies of water comes from the air. Although a small amount of atmospheric oxygen dissolves on simple contact with the surface, much more may be dissolved with mechanical mixing by the turbulence of waves, waterfalls, whirlpools and rapids. (See the photograph on page 13.) The air, however, does not account for all the oxygen dissolved in water. Some is produced by green water-plants in a process called photosynthesis. Photosynthesis (from the Greek *photos* – of light, and *synthesis* – putting together) is a series of chemical reactions involving light, chlorophyll and carbon dioxide, whereby all green plants produce their own carbohydrate and protein nutrients plus oxygen.

Experiment 3.2
Photosynthesis

Set up apparatus similar to that shown in Figure 3-2. Shine the light until a full test tube of gas has been collected. (A 60-watt bulb is enough.) Test the gas with a glowing splint.

In this experiment it takes a long time to collect a full test tube of oxygen simply because the reaction is a slow one, not because a lot of the oxygen goes into solution. As we have seen, it takes only about 9 ppm or 9 mg of oxygen per litre (dm^3) of water for oxygen saturation at room temperature $(20°C)$.

The complicated process of photosynthesis can be expressed in the following equation.

$$\text{Carbon dioxide} + \text{water} \longrightarrow \text{carbohydrate} + \text{oxygen}$$
$$6CO_2 + 6H_2O \longrightarrow C_6H_{12}O_6 + 6O_2$$

This reaction will take place only in green plants in the presence of light. If there is insufficient light, at night for instance, the reaction will not occur.

The green colour in plants comes from chlorophyll. Without this chemical, photosynthesis will not occur either.

Photosynthesis in clear water occurs only within about 27 m of the surface, as this is the limit to which sunlight can penetrate with sufficient intensity. The main producers of oxygen in water are tiny green one-celled plants, called *algae*, and other *phytoplankton* – the name given to all floating plant organisms, some of which can be quite large (seaweed). Even though trees and other land plants produce oxygen by photosynthesis, it has been estimated that about 50 per cent of atmospheric oxygen replacement comes from water plants, and most of this from algae and other phytoplankton.

We have seen that photosynthesis in nature depends on the presence of *sunlight, water* (or water vapour), *carbon dioxide*, and, of course, *living plants* containing *chlorophyll*. Where does the carbon dioxide come from?

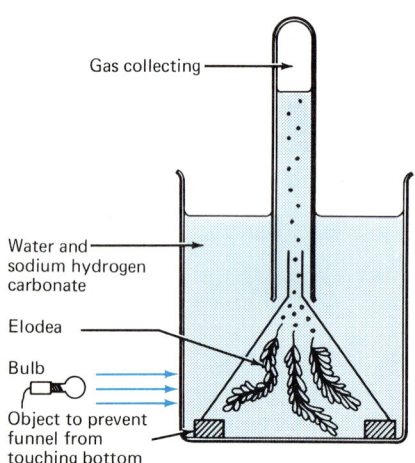

Gas collecting

Water and sodium hydrogen carbonate

Elodea

Bulb

Object to prevent funnel from touching bottom

Figure 3-2. Elodea is a very good photosynthesizer. Why is the sodium hydrogen carbonate necessary?

Respiration and combustion

All living things obtain their energy from a process called respiration (Figure 3-3). This is the complete reverse of the photosynthesis reaction:

$$\text{carbohydrate} + \text{oxygen} \longrightarrow \text{carbon dioxide} + \text{water} + \text{energy}$$
$$C_6H_{12}O_6 + 6O_2 \longrightarrow 6CO_2 + 6H_2O$$

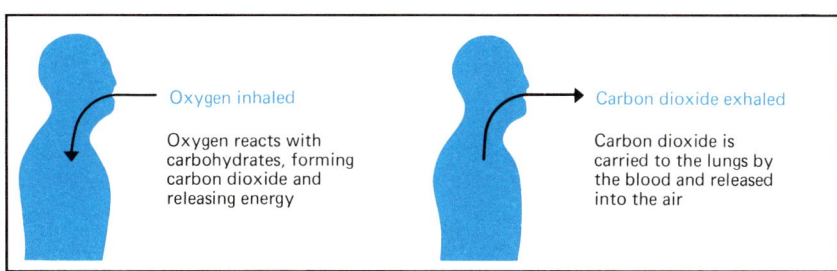

Oxygen inhaled

Oxygen reacts with carbohydrates, forming carbon dioxide and releasing energy

Carbon dioxide exhaled

Carbon dioxide is carried to the lungs by the blood and released into the air

Figure 3-3. Respiration.

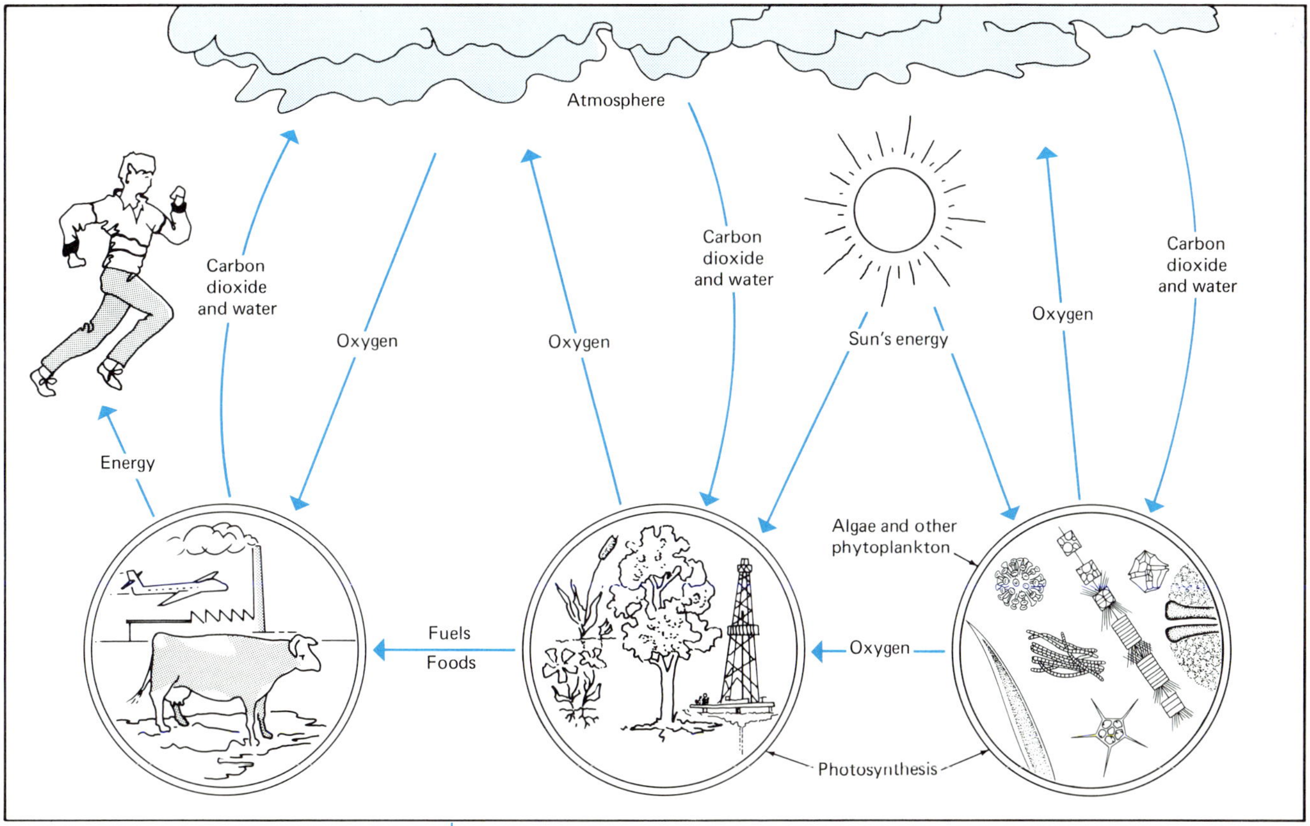

Atmosphere

Carbon dioxide and water

Oxygen

Oxygen

Carbon dioxide and water

Sun's energy

Oxygen

Carbon dioxide and water

Energy

Algae and other phytoplankton

Fuels
Foods

Oxygen

Photosynthesis

Figure 3-4. The carbon cycle. Oxygen is used up by the processes shown and is produced by green plants. How do plants get their energy?

Can you see that the energy we obtain by eating carbohydrates depends ultimately on light and heat energy from the sun?

An automobile engine also 'respires,' using fossil fuels and oxygen and producing carbon dioxide, water vapour, and energy, among other things.

octane + oxygen $\longrightarrow$ carbon dioxide + water + energy

$$C_8H_{18} + 12\tfrac{1}{2}O_2 \longrightarrow 8CO_2 + 9H_2O$$

Plants are also living things and require energy. In light they respire *and* photosynthesize, but in the absence of light they only respire. Fortunately for man, plants produce slightly more oxygen through photosynthesis than they need for their own respiration. This provides a constant supply of oxygen in bodies of water and in the air. Excess production of oxygen over consumption is 1 part in 10 000. (See Figure 3-4.)

Experiment 3.3
Carbon dioxide in combustion

Float a small lit candle on a watch glass in a pneumatic trough. Measure the height of a large beaker. Place the beaker carefully over the watch glass so that no air can enter. Hold the beaker until the candle goes out and then raise the beaker until its mouth is level with the surface of the water. (See Figure 3-5.) Measure the height of the water inside the beaker. Calculate the percentage decrease in volume of the gases inside the beaker.

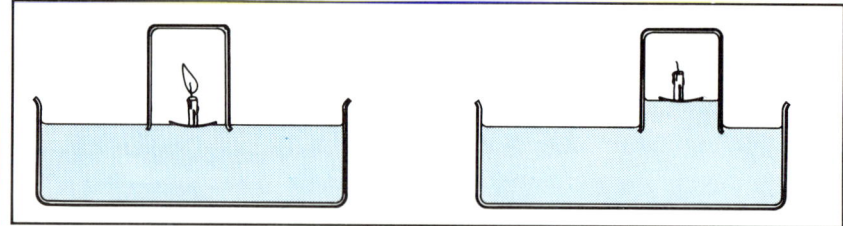

Figure 3-5. 'Before' and 'after' in Experiment 3.3.

Candle wax is a hydrocarbon and has a formula similar to that of gasoline. When candle wax burns, oxygen gas from the air is converted into carbon dioxide gas and steam. On cooling, the steam condenses into water. But what happens to the carbon dioxide? It does not condense, but dissolves in the water. The atmosphere and the respiration and decomposition of all aquatic plant and animal life are the main sources of the dissolved carbon dioxide needed by green water-plants to perform photosynthesis.

Water and the nitrogen problem

Seventy-eight per cent of the earth's atmosphere is nitrogen. It is a very inactive gas and helps to dilute the oxygen in the atmosphere and slow down rates of combustion and respiration. Nitrogen is an essential element in proteins and all protein nitrogen comes from the atmosphere.

The problem is that the nitrogen molecule, N_2, is very stable. A large amount of energy is needed to separate one nitrogen atom from the other and let them combine with other atoms.

Nitrogen gas itself cannot enter directly into the formation of proteins, but combined with another element it can. This combined nitrogen is referred to as 'fixed' nitrogen. Examples of fixed nitrogen are the nitrate ion, NO_3^-, the ammonium ion, NH_4^+, and the ammonia molecule, NH_3. Fixed nitrogen is acted upon by plants and converted into protein.

Certain bacteria in the soil can fix nitrogen directly from the air. Leguminous plants, too, such as beans and clover, grow nitrogen-fixing nodules on their roots. For centuries farmers have practised crop rotation. In each field, every three or four years they sow a crop of legumes so that the soil is replenished with nitrogen.

In water, blue-green algae can fix atmospheric nitrogen – dissolved in the same way as atmospheric oxygen.

Experiment 3.4
Fixing nitrogen
by lightning

Set up the apparatus shown in Figure 3-7. Let the spark pass for about 10 minutes. Hold a piece of white paper behind the flask. What do you notice? Carefully smell the contents. Have you ever smelled a gas like that before? Shake the contents and test with blue litmus.

The brown colour you saw was nitrogen dioxide gas.

$$\text{Nitrogen} + \text{oxygen} \longrightarrow \text{nitrogen dioxide}$$
$$N_2 + 2O_2 \longrightarrow 2NO_2$$

Figure 3-6. These are nitrogen-fixing nodules on soybean roots. Soybean exports were banned from the U.S.A. in a food crisis in 1973. Can you think of a reason why?

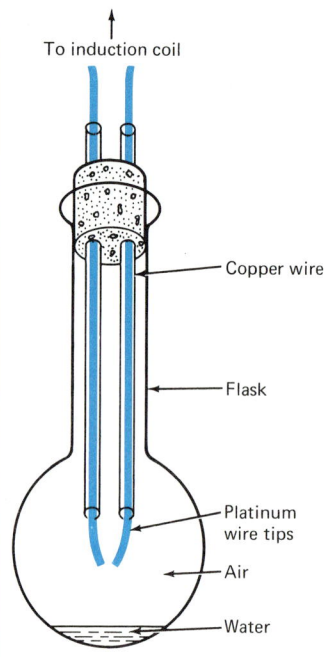

To induction coil

Copper wire

Flask

Platinum wire tips

Air

Water

The spark fixed some of the nitrogen molecules by combining each of them with two oxygen molecules. Lightning does this in the atmosphere. Then,

nitrogen dioxide + water $\longrightarrow$ nitric acid + nitrogen monoxide

$$3NO_2 + H_2O \longrightarrow 2HNO_3 + NO$$

and, nitrogen monoxide + oxygen $\longrightarrow$ nitrogen dioxide

$$2NO + O_2 \longrightarrow 2NO_2$$

The nitrogen dioxide combines with water vapour to form dilute nitric acid which comes down to earth in rain. The presence of nitric acid explains why the blue litmus turned red in Experiment 3.4.

There are, therefore, three natural ways in which fixed nitrogen can enter the soil to become a component of the proteins necessary for plant growth. What are these ways?

It was not until just before World War I that a large-scale artificial method of fixing nitrogen was developed. Other processes had been discovered but were not commercially successful. Fritz Haber, a German chemist, succeeded in combining nitrogen from the air with hydrogen obtained by passing steam over heated coke:

$$H_2O + C \longrightarrow CO + H_2$$

The nitrogen and the hydrogen combine at a pressure of 100 MPa (megapascals) and a temperature of 500°C. Even under these extreme conditions the reaction is slow and incomplete, and an iron catalyst is necessary to speed up the process.

$$N_2 + 3H_2 \rightleftharpoons 2NH_3$$

The reaction is reversible; some of the ammonia always decomposes into the original elements. Today most of the ammonia produced is used in making chemical fertilizers.

It might seem that the vast quantities of nitrogen in the air could be used to end the world's shortage of protein once and for all. Unfortunately, about twenty tonnes of coke are needed to fix seven tonnes of atmospheric nitrogen. This makes fertilizer costly. Coal and other hydrocarbon resources of the Earth are not unlimited. Although the protein problem has been partially solved, the solution may well be only temporary.

Nitrates such a sodium nitrate and potassium nitrate are an important ingredient in the production of explosives. In World War I, Germany's supply of nitrates (Chile saltpetre) was cut off by the British naval blockade. The Haber process was greatly expanded and it seemed that Germany's problems were solved. This did not come about. In 1917 and 1918 the harvests were disastrous, mainly because most of the nitrates produced were used to make explosives and not fertilizers. Ironically, the country that solved the nitrogen problem saw its people starve for lack of fertilizer! This was a contributing factor to Germany's defeat in 1918.

Experiment 3.5
Solubility of fertilizers

Place a few crystals of each of the following chemicals separately into 6 clean test tubes half-filled with distilled water: calcium nitrate, zinc nitrate, ammonium nitrate, sodium nitrate, ammonium sulfate, and ammonium phosphate. Shake the contents, and add pieces of red and blue litmus paper to each test tube.

What conclusions can you draw about the solubility of nitrates and ammonium compounds? What is the pH of ammonium compounds?

To be absorbed by a plant's roots, fertilizers must be soluble in water. If they are too soluble, however, they are washed away with the natural drainage. In acid soils, certain bacteria are able to convert fixed nitrogen into free nitrogen gas. They are called denitrifying bacteria. In both cases there is a loss of precious fixed nitrogen.

The nitrogen cycle

The products of respiration and combustion — carbon dioxide and water vapour — are gaseous, and the carbon cycle (Figure 3-4) is easily completed. But what happens to the products of protein digestion?

The waste products of protein digestion are mainly urea and uric acid and are passed out of the body in the urine. The nitrogen in these substances is in a fixed state. Much energy is expended in fixing the nitrogen molecules. For this reason, fixed nitrogen is precious and should not be wasted. It should be re-used as fertilizer. But does this happen?

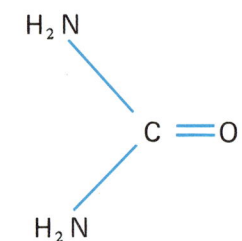

This is the urea molecule.

Figure 3-9. The nitrogen cycle. This diagram shows the passage of nitrogen atoms from the air to plants, animals and humans, and from humans through the sewage system, to rivers and lakes.

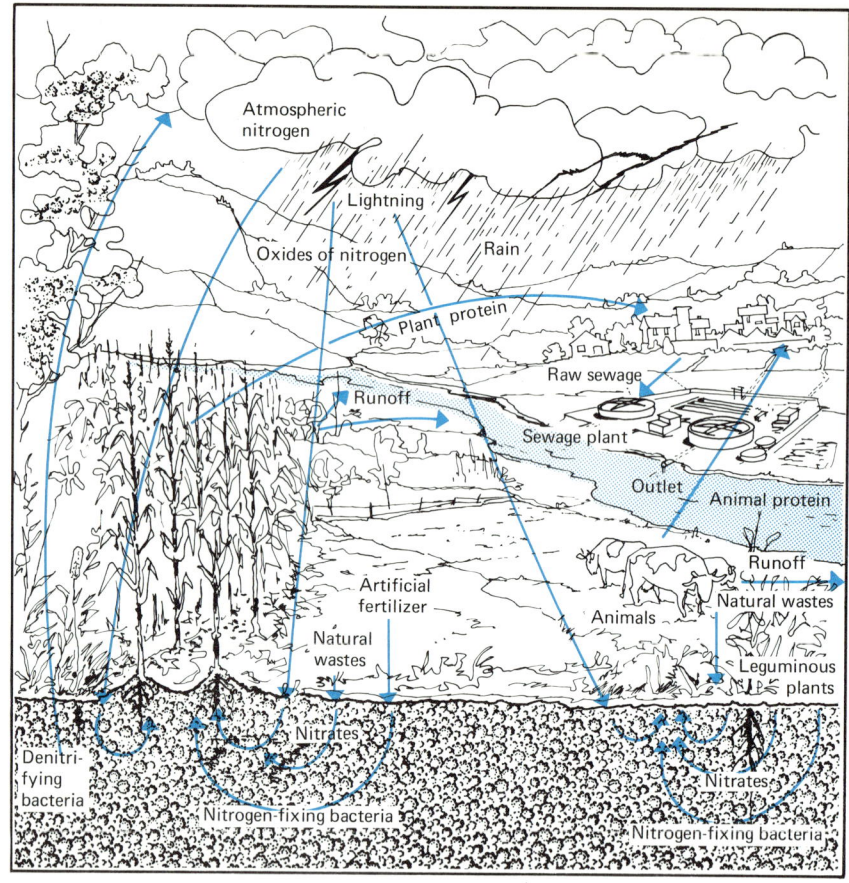

The Dead Sea contains as much as 7 to 10 times the amount of dissolved matter as ordinary sea water.

Consider what happens to the human waste-products of protein digestion. They are flushed down the drains, into the sewage systems and finally into lakes, rivers and other bodies of water.

In Experiment 3.5 you saw that ammonium compounds and nitrates are soluble in water. They are, therefore, very difficult to extract from sewage. Another problem is that wastes from the proteins you eat might end up in water thousands of kilometres away from where the food was grown. This is very different from the carbon cycle, where the waste products are gaseous and hence can be spread all over the Earth.

The direct use of human waste-products as fertilizer can prove dangerous because of the potentially harmful bacteria present. The accumulation of heavy metals in sewage plant residues often prevents these wastes also from being used as fertilizer.

Can you see why flushing dyed toilet paper is more polluting than flushing white paper?

Phosphorus and phosphates

Nitrates, phosphates, and pollution

Fixed nitrogen in the form of ammonia is used in other industries as well as in making fertilizer. It is used in the manufacture of plastics such as bakelite, fibres such as nylon, and also in synthetic dyes and explosives. Trinitrotoluene (TNT) and nitroglycerine both contain fixed nitrogen.

Phosphorus also is a vital element for growth and body metabolism. (Figure 3-10.) Phosphorus comes from rocks containing calcium phosphate and other phosphates. The phosphates that are soluble are washed into the soil and absorbed by plants. (Figure 3-11.)

Chemists extract phosphates from the earth and process them into fertilizers. Most of the phosphates we excrete end up, like the nitrates, in rivers, lakes and oceans. Unfortunately the supply of phosphate rock is low and it is non-renewable.

Nitrates and phosphates dissolved in water are plant nutrients. In bodies of water they stimulate the growth of algae and other phytoplankton. These are very useful because they produce oxygen by photosynthesis and are food for water animals.

Figure 3-10. Tomato plants growing without phosphorus or without nitrogen. Note that they do not grow as well as the plant that receives all the essential nutrients. They are also more likely to become diseased than 'normal' plants.

Figure 3-11. The phosphorus 'cycle'.
Unfortunately most phosphorus is not
recycled back to the earth but passes
into rivers, lakes and oceans.

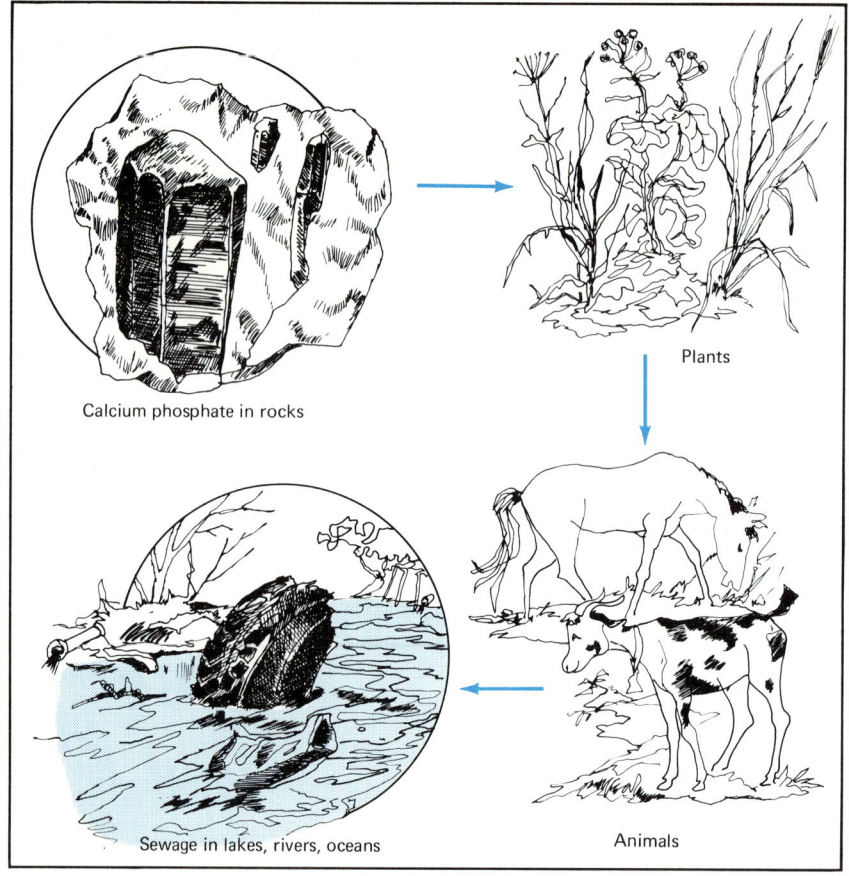

Calcium phosphate in rocks

Plants

Sewage in lakes, rivers, oceans

Animals

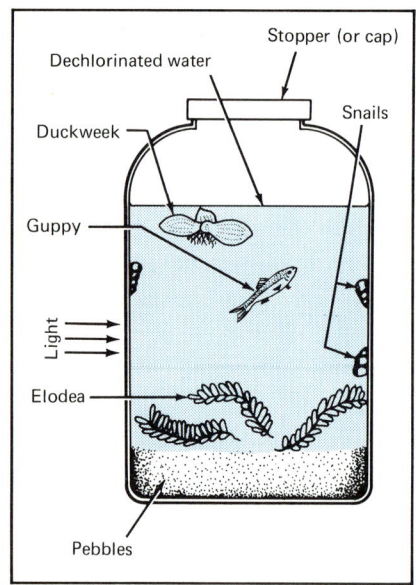

Stopper (or cap)

Dechlorinated water

Duckweek

Snails

Guppy

Light

Elodea

Pebbles

Figure 3-12. Equipment for Experiment 3.6.

Experiment 3.6
Growing algae blooms

Normally the nitrates and phosphates are provided by the excreta of water animals and by decaying plants. This is part of the 'balance of nature'. However, excessive phosphates and nitrates — from sewage and fertilizers — upset this balance. The result is algae 'bloom'. (Figure 3-13.) Some of the single plants that make up this bloom can be distinguished in Figure 3-14.

Set up the arrangement shown in Figure 3-12. (After a few weeks the water will become cloudy and green. This is an algae bloom.) Perform the experiment again with a few grams of calcium nitrate added to the water, and then again with a few grams of ammonium phosphate added instead. Is there a difference in what happens?

The pollution problem starts when excessive quantities of algae and plankton die. Bacteria need oxygen to decompose these dead plants and animals. If the oxygen used by the bacteria cannot be replaced quickly enough, the oxygen content of the water (see Experiment 3.1) falls. The severe oxygen shortage in Lake Erie is largely a result of this cause.

Figure 3-13 (right). One result of eutrophication. The algae cover almost the whole surface of the stream.

Figure 3-14 far right). These are algae, or microscopic water plants. Normally they are a valuable source of food and oxygen, but if they become too numerous they are a serious pollutant when they die.

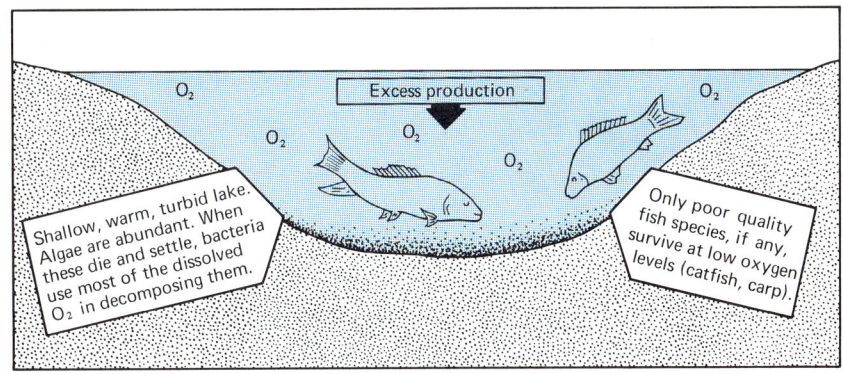

Shallow, warm, turbid lake. Algae are abundant. When these die and settle, bacteria use most of the dissolved O_2 in decomposing them.

Excess production

Only poor quality fish species, if any, survive at low oxygen levels (catfish, carp).

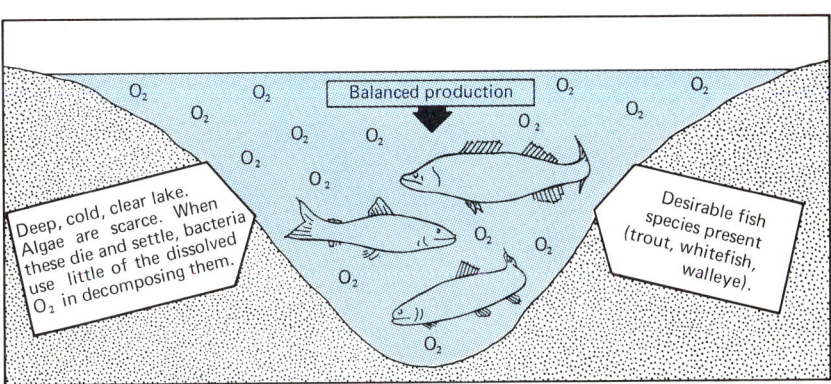

Deep, cold, clear lake. Algae are scarce. When these die and settle, bacteria use little of the dissolved O_2 in decomposing them.

Balanced production

Desirable fish species present (trout, whitefish, walleye).

Figure 3-15 (upper). A eutrophic lake. (Lower). A 'well-balanced' lake.

This *eutrophication* of water is one of the main problems that inland water authorities are trying to solve. (Eutrophication may be defined as the intentional or unintentional *enrichment* of a body of water. Enrichment is the addition of excessive amounts of essential plant nutrients such as phosphorus and nitrogen.) Not only is it wasteful to discharge nitrates and phosphates into the water in the form of human wastes or detergents, but it is harmful to water life as well. (See page 11.)

Another problem: fats and carbohydrates

Undigested fats and carbohydrates are also human waste-products. They are classed as organic wastes. Again, oxygen is required to decompose them into simpler forms. Here is yet another cause of oxygen depletion.

Biochemical oxygen demand (B.O.D.)

Fresh water approaching a sewage outlet usually has a normal dissolved oxygen level. After the addition of the sewage, the dissolved oxygen content will not change much immediately, but now the water is polluted and has an oxygen 'demand'. The oxygen content of the water will start to fall as it is used by bacteria decomposing the pollutants. Chemists call this demand the biochemical oxygen demand, or B.O.D.

Experiment 3.7
Measuring B.O.D.

Collect various samples of contaminated water, maybe from nearby pools or from Experiment 3.6. Completely fill the B.O.D. bottles (capacity $250\,cm^3$) with the samples. Make sure that there is no bubble of air in the top of the bottle.

Add $1\,cm^3$ of methylene blue solution to each sample, making sure that the tip of the pipette is well below the surface of the water. Store the samples in a dark place, and keep the temperature as near to $20°C$ as possible.

Check the bottles every 24 hours (or twice a day if possible) and record when the blue colour disappears. Calculate the total time required for the blue colour to disappear from each sample.

Methylene blue keeps its colour in the presence of oxygen, but is colourless when there is no oxygen.

Table 3-1 tells you the percentage of the biochemical oxygen demand that has been satisfied. For example, if the blue colour disappeared after five days, there was enough oxygen in the sample to satisfy 68 per cent of the total B.O.D. This means that 32 per cent was unsatisfied. The longer the blue colour takes to disappear, the less polluted is the sample; the quicker the blue colour disappears, the more polluted is the sample.

Table 3-1 INCUBATION (DAYS) NEEDED FOR DISAPPEARANCE OF BLUE COLOUR AT 20°C	
Days	percentage of B.O.D. satisfied
0.5	11
1.0	21
2.0	37
3.0	50
4.0	60
5.0	68
6.0	75
7.0	80
8.0	84
9.0	87
10.0	90

The B.O.D. is a good measure of the extent of water pollution, and is the most widely performed test in water-control laboratories. Controlling authorities often base their standards on a measurement called the 5-day B.O.D.

Take 2 samples of contaminated water. Do a Winkler test on one sample. (Experiment 3.1) Keep the other sample in a dark place and give it the Winkler test 5 days later.

The difference between the two readings is the 5-day B.O.D. measured in parts per million. A 5-day B.O.D. of 7 ppm, for instance, means that 7 mg of oxygen were consumed by 1 dm^3 of the contaminated water over a period of 5 days.

There are two complications in using this test.

(1) If your samples in Experiment 3.8 are too polluted, you will have a zero reading in your second Winkler test. To find the correct B.O.D., dilute each sample by the same amount and make a dilution correction. If you diluted your samples by 50 per cent, then

$$\text{5-day B.O.D.} = \frac{\text{D.O. before} - \text{D.O. five days later}}{50} \times 100$$

D.O. stands for dissolved oxygen.

(2) The five-day period is chosen because most sewage can be broken down in this time. Some pollutants – wood shavings for instance – do not break down in five days. Thus, if a B.O.D. test is made on water containing wood shavings, a low reading will be obtained; but the shavings are still combining with oxygen. You can get a better idea of their polluting capabilities from Experiment 3.7.

Untreated sewage has a B.O.D. of about 300 ppm. On page 27 is a case study showing how the B.O.D. test was used to help pin-point a source of pollution.

Bacteria

Human faeces contain potentially harmful bacteria. Bacteria also exist in air and in water. Some are dangerous, some are not; but normally they are all a natural part of the ecological system.

With the exception of fresh urine, human waste products can be hazardous to health. Bacteria break down these waste products into simpler substances, rendering them harmless. Bacteria are decomposers. They multiply quickly in a nutritious medium such as sewage. They break down sewage, using up oxygen in the process. This is as it should be – until there is too much sewage! Then the water becomes depleted of dissolved oxygen.

This experiment must be done with the utmost care, as bacteria can easily be transferred to your body. Before you start the experiment, study the safety procedures recommended by the manufacturer of the apparatus you will use. The equipment is shown in Figure 3-16. Follow the manufacturer's instructions.

Filter the sewage in the Millipore apparatus provided. Transfer the filter to the nutrient medium. The number of bacterial colonies counted equals the number of single bacteria present in the original sample. If too many colonies are produced, then you will have to dilute the original sample. This test is known as the coliform count.

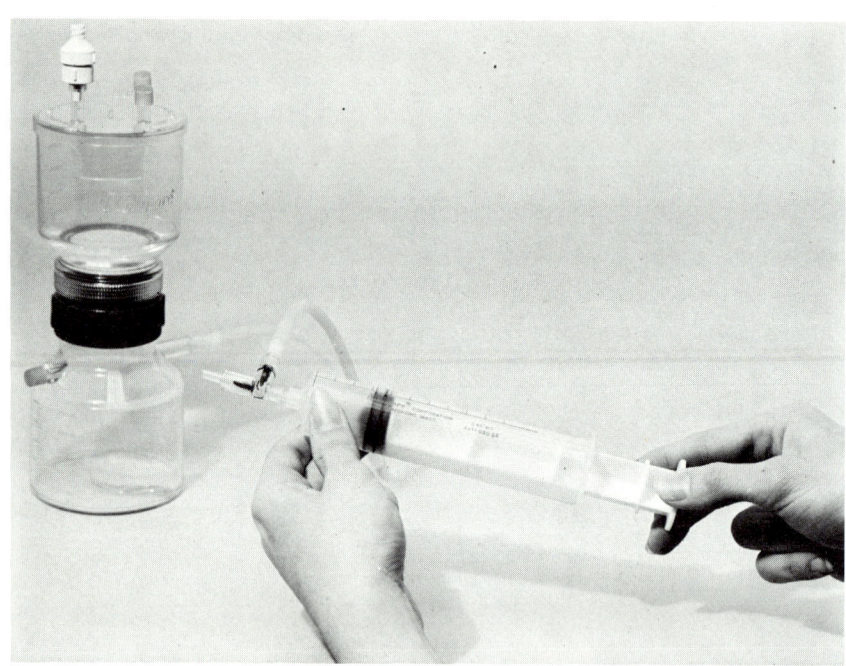

Figure 3-16. This is the Millipore filtering apparatus used in Experiment 3.9.

There are many bacteria in water. The species tested for in Experiment 3.9 was *Escherichia coli* (*E. coli*). If *E. coli* is present the water is likely contaminated with faecal bacteria. *E. coli* itself is not dangerous, but a positive result indicates that dangerous bacteria may also be present. While it is relatively easy to test for *E. coli*, it is difficult to test for the other bacteria. The filter catches the *E. coli*, which grow and multiply on the medium just as they do in sewage.

The Canadian federal government has ruled that drinking water must not contain more than 4 coliforms per 100 cm^3. Water with more than 100 coliforms per 100 cm^3 is considered dangerous for swimming. (Be cautious about opening your mouth while swimming in unchlorinated water.)

The diseases triggered by bacteria in untreated sewage are principally typhoid, cholera, and dysentery. Find out about epidemics of these diseases, particularly in past centuries. Note the unsanitary practices of those times.

A case from the files

Mr. X, who caught and sold minnows to fishermen, found that the fish in his minnowtraps were dying. An official investigation showed that the deaths resulted from the contamination of the stream by wastes from a beef-cattle and hog farm owned by Mr. Y. (See Figure 3-17 and Table 3-2.) The fish were killed by suffocation because of the low oxygen content in the river. This was caused by the farm's effluent.

The farmer was asked to install a waste treatment system to stop the runoff from the farmyard entering the stream. He dug a lagoon bed to collect the wastes and used them to spray-irrigate and fertilize his land. Mr. X's minnows survived, and Mr. Y got cheap fertilizer — a perfect example of applying ecological principles to mutual benefit.

Figure 3-17 (below). Testing stations.

Figure 3-18 (below, right). Runoff from Mr. Y's property (left photograph) led to the formation of the growth in the photograph on the right.

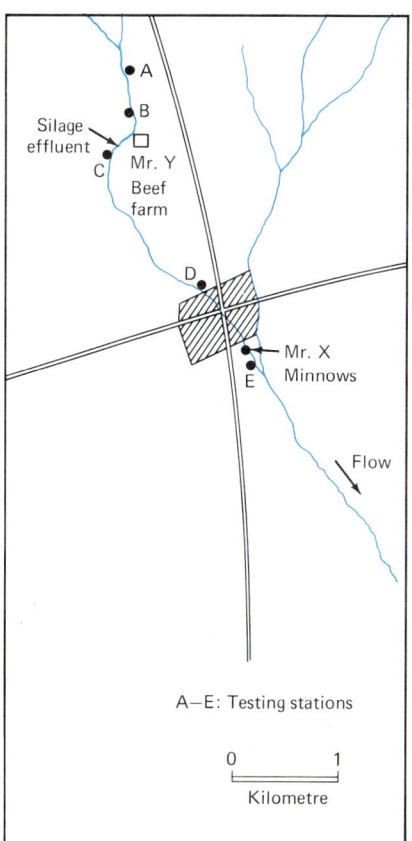

Table 3-2 CHEMICAL ANALYSIS RESULTS

	B.O.D. in ppm (Expt. 3.8)	Total phosphorus in ppm	Total nitrogen in ppm	pH	D.O. in ppm (Expt. 3.1)
A	1.0	0.03	0.40	8.5	10.0
B	40.0	0.64	2.60	6.8	3.6
C	50 000.0	2 300.00	2 300.00	4.0	10.0
D	42.0	0.76	2.40	7.8	1.2
E	30.0	0.66	3.00	7.8	4.0

Total phosphorus measures *all* the phosphorus present. Total nitrogen measures *all* the fixed nitrogen present. *All* means from all sources and in all forms.

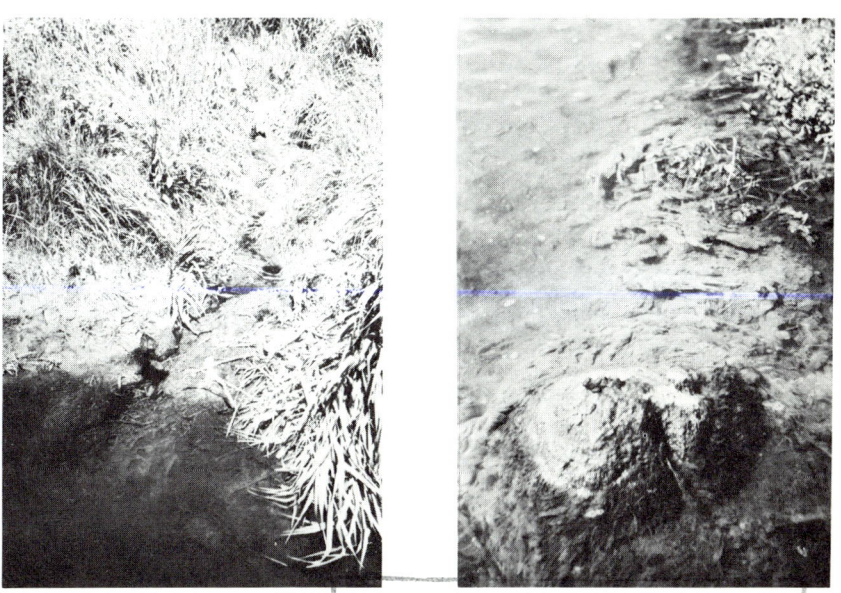

4
Industrial pollution

In Chapter 3 you studied pollution caused by humans and other animals. In recent times, because more and more people live in cities, this form of pollution has become a serious problem in waterways where sewage is discharged. Natural waters need time to deal with these wastes, but less time is needed if elaborate sewage treatment systems are used. (See Chapter 5.)

Industrial pollution is a different problem. Inorganic chemicals are dumped into the waters, sometimes quickly and in large amounts. The waters frequently cannot handle these substances which are often poisonous to living things.

Many industrial plants are hundreds of kilometres away from heavily populated areas where there are likely to be adequate sewage treatment systems. The nearest river usually becomes a convenient drain for wastes, which are often inadequately treated.

With pulp and paper mills, the most obvious pollutant is wood shavings and bark. These have a large B.O.D. Cellulose, the main carbohydrate in wood, breaks down slowly, and thence the oxygen demand lasts for a long time. Another pollutant is sulfite liquor, used by mills as a bleaching agent.

Experiment 4.1
Sulfite pollution

Add a few crystals of sodium sulfite to 25 cm³ of distilled water in an Erlenmeyer flask. Make 50 cm³ of 0.1 mol·dm⁻³ solution of potassium manganate (VII). Add to this 5 cm³ of dilute sulfuric acid.

Add the acidified manganate(VII) solution from a burette to the sulfite solution. What happens to the purple colour of the manganate(VII) solution? Keep adding the manganate(VII) solution until the colour stays purple.

What has happened in this experiment? Acidified potassium manganate(VII) is an oxidizing agent:

$$2KMnO_4 \longrightarrow K_2O + 2MnO + 5(O)$$

The excess oxygen reacts with the sulfite ion:
$$SO_3{}^{2-}(aq) + (O) \longrightarrow SO_4{}^{2-}(aq)$$

This shows that sulfite ions will reduce the oxygen concentration in the water into which they are released.

A third form of pollution from pulp mills is mercury. Mercury compounds are good fungicides and are used to prevent fungal growth on the pulp. Small but dangerous quantities do enter many waterways.

Nuclear energy

The world is rapidly running out of many sources of energy. Fossil fuels, coal and oil, for instance, can be used only once. Hydro-electric plants, also, have maximum potential outputs, and suitable undeveloped sites in the industrialized nations are few. While the reserves of some fuels are diminishing, demand for them continues to increase.

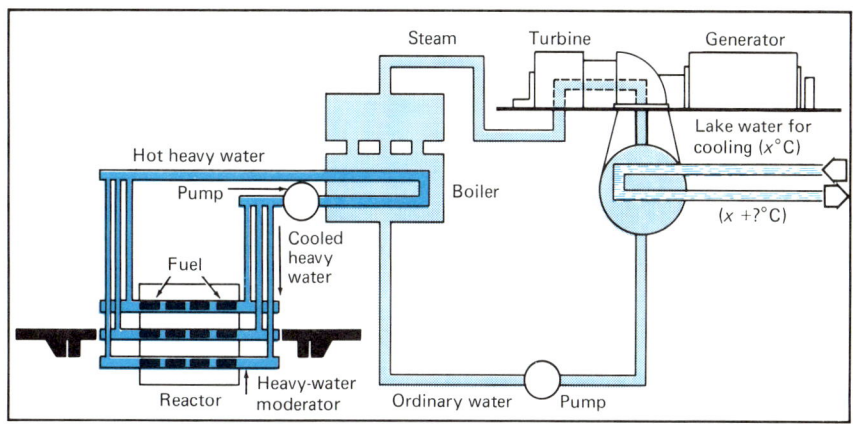

Figure 4-1. The CANDU-PHW (Canada Deuterium Uranium-Pressurized Heavy Water) system for atomic reactors. Note the three water system:

(1) ▬ heavy water;
(2) ▬ ordinary water;
(3) ▬ lake water.

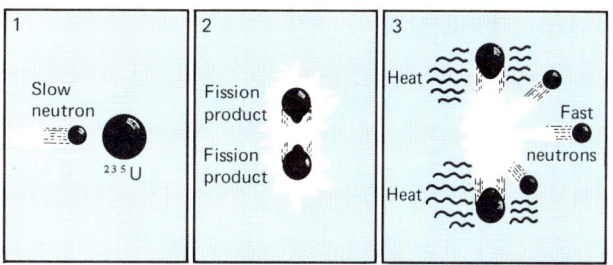
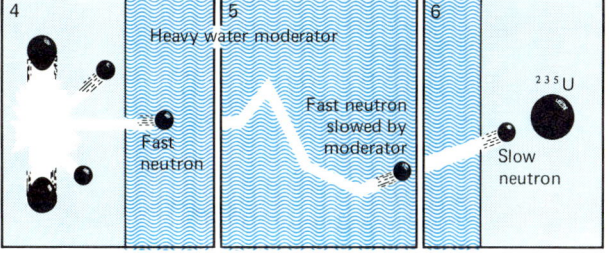

Figure 4-2. The slow neutron splits the nucleus of the uranium atom in two and produces extra-fast neutrons and heat energy. The fast neutrons are slowed down by the heavy water so that they can cause another fission.

What can be done? Technology is not yet advanced enough to convert energy from the sun or from the fusion of hydrogen atoms on a scale large enough to satisfy the needs of modern industry; but nuclear energy using the uranium-fission process is proving to be a partial solution. The trouble is that nuclear power stations need vast quantities of cooling water because of the high temperatures produced. (See Figure 4-1.) The temperature of the discharged water is sometimes as much as 5°C higher than the water into which it is being discharged. The consequent rise in temperature of this water increases its percentage oxygen saturation (see page 14), and if the water is already at or near saturation, its dissolved oxygen *content* is actually *decreased*.

In an atomic pile the basic reaction is the splitting of ^{235}U atoms by firing neutrons at them. (See Figure 4-2.) The uranium atom splits into two fragments and releases neutrons and energy. An example is:

$$^{235}_{92}U + {}^{1}_{0}n \longrightarrow {}^{143}_{54}Xe + {}^{90}_{38}Sr + 3{}^{1}_{0}n + energy$$

The uranium atom can split into different fragments, but the combined mass of the products is always less than that of the reactants. The lost mass has been turned into energy according to Einstein's equation

$$E = mc^2$$

where E = energy produced, m = mass destroyed, and c = speed of light. The energy produced turns water into steam which drives the turbines of electricity generators. (See Figure 1-1.)

A more serious pollution problem resulting from nuclear fission is the disposal of radioactive wastes. They are usually buried or dumped into the ocean. Neither method is a good one because these wastes have a very long half-life and will remain radioactive for thousands of years.

Toxic metals and pesticides

Pesticides and toxic metals usually kill. DDT kills malaria-carrying insects and crop pests. Mercury kills fungus; copper sulfate kills snails, and arsenic kills almost anything.

Some pesticide poisons are not easily broken down and can remain toxic long after their intended job has been done. For instance, insects killed by DDT are eaten by birds. DDT can get into water and so contaminate fish and birds — and the people who eat them. DDT has even been found in penguins in the Antarctic. Some birds that have eaten DDT become infertile or lay eggs with shells so thin that they are prone to breakage. So great are the dangers of DDT, that its use has now been largely banned. Despite its harmful effects, however, DDT has, on balance, been beneficial to mankind. It has reduced disease and has increased crop yields sometimes many fold.

Mercury poisoning

Perhaps you have heard the expression 'mad as a hatter' or have read of the Mad Hatter in *Alice In Wonderland*. In the eighteenth and nineteenth centuries 'nitrate of mercury' (mercury(II) nitrate, $Hg(NO_3)_2$) was used in making felt for hats. An unfortunate result was the mercury was absorbed by hatmakers and the expression 'mad as a hatter' was at times all too true.

In bodies of water mercury does not remain as a silvery liquid metal. It will form ethyl and methyl mercury which can be ingested by fish. And the fish are eaten by people. . . . In recent years industry, in some places, has succeeded in greatly reducing the amounts of waste mercury discharged into water systems. However, even small quantities are dangerous.

Here is some information about mercury.
(1) A dose of 1 g of mercuric salts can be fatal to humans.
(2) Fish to be safe for eating should contain less than 5 ppm mercury.

In 1969 fish from the St. Clair River between Lakes Huron and Erie were found to contain 7 to 8 ppm mercury. Fishing in Lake St. Clair and the St. Clair River was banned. The result — unemployment. (Note: not all the mercury in water is put there by industry.)

(3) If you ingested 100 mg of organic mercury, it would not be distributed evenly throughout your body. About 50 mg would concentrate in the liver, 20 mg in the brain (scientists consider dangerous 2 mg of mercury per gram of brain, and the average brain weighs 1 360 g), and 30 mg throughout various other organs and tissues. It would take 150 days for 10 mg to disappear from the brain, but only 50 days for 25 mg to disappear from the liver. Half of the 100 mg would still be in the body after 70 days.

Mercury poisoning in humans is relatively rare. However, mercury kills life in the water and this life is part of ecological cycles. If, for example, algae die of poisoning, an important food supply and an important source of oxygen are lost.

Suspended and dissolved solids

Suspended solids in water consist of living and dead plants and animals, silt, sewage, and some industrial wastes.

Experiment 4.2 Total suspended solids (TSS)

Record the mass of a filter paper (with as small a pore size as possible) and filter exactly 1 dm^3 of contaminated water. Allow the filter paper to dry completely and reweigh it. Note: as the difference in mass will be quite small, any outside influence can have an appreciable effect. The result in milligrams per cubic decimetre (of water) gives the total suspended solids in the contaminated water sample in parts per million. Or, as we say, it gives the TSS in ppm. Note: with liquids other than water, this would not be so. Water is a special case: 1 dm^3 of distilled water at 3.98°C (4°C) and standard pressure has a mass of exactly 1 kg; and 1 dm^3 of impure water at normal room temperatures and pressures would weigh virtually the same — 1 kg for most practical purposes. Therefore in any sample of water, an impurity concentration of x mg·dm^{-3} is considered to be equivalent to x mg·kg^{-1}, or x ppm. Note: Suspended solids do not include soluble matter. Sodium chloride, for instance, will go through the filter paper.

Experiment 4.3 Total dissolved solids (TDS)

The following method is not very accurate either, but nevertheless should give worthwhile results. Record the mass of a thoroughly clean 250 cm^3 beaker. Add 100 cm^3 of filtered water. Wash the now empty container with distilled water and add the washings also to the beaker. Evaporate to dryness at about 103°C in a dust-free oven. Allow the beaker to cool and record its mass again.

The difference between the two mass readings multiplied by 10 gives the TDS in ppm. If you obtain almost the same results in repeating the experiment twice, your test should be reasonably accurate.

Figure 4-3. This improvised "slick-licker" was quickly built to clean up oily water when an oil tanker, the Arrow, went down in Chedabucto Bay, Nova Scotia, in 1970.

The results of Experiments 4.2 and 4.3 give a good indication of the state of pollution of water. If the TDS value is less than 100 ppm, the water is considered unable to support life because it does not have enough nutrients. Treated sewage effluent can have TDS values between 300 and 400 ppm.

If the suspended solids are silty, they will reflect the sun's rays, and the water plants will not receive enough sunlight for photosynthesis. If the suspended solids are organic, they will raise the normal B.O.D. and thus will rob the water of dissolved oxygen.

In general, suspended organic solids are algae and other phytoplankton. When their numbers grow abnormally large through the presence of excess nutrients in dissolved solids (enrichment), their death rate increases. The bacteria that are associated with them then start breaking them down into simpler substances, using up oxygen in the process.

Oil

"Between 1 000 000 and 1 000 000-000 tonnes of oil are added to the oceans each year."

Environment Canada

If an oil tanker springs a leak or washes out its tanks at sea or crashes and spills its load, damage can be very serious. Oil is a mixture of hydrocarbons and floats on water (see Experiment 6.5). As a result sunlight and oxygen are cut off. Oil takes a long time to decompose and hence can wash up onto beaches and into harbours. If the slick is removed by detergents, the detergents can cause more damage than the oil itself.

If birds get oil on their feathers they are usually doomed because, even if it is washed off with soap, a water-repellent coating on the feathers is often removed with it, and the bird cannot float. Sometimes birds try to eat the oil in an effort to clean their feathers, often with fatal results.

Perhaps you can understand why there is such fierce debate about the continued building of giant supertankers for transporting oil all over the world. Even overland pipelines, while less hazardous, threaten to disrupt delicately balanced ecologies.

A sickly river

A river in southern Canada was sick. In fact the water in some parts was almost dead. Yet some stretches seemed to be quite healthy. What was causing the trouble?

A provincial government team set out to find the reason. Testing stations were set up in and around a city of 50 000 people, which had grown up where a side stream joined the river. Figure 4-4 shows where some of the testing stations were placed. Note how the scientists tested the water at the outskirts of the city, at spots within it, downstream of the community and at the point where treated wastes from its sewage plant were discharged into the river.

At the time industrial wastes with a high B.O.D. were also discharged into the river by several industrial companies above station C. Caustic cleaning water was poured into the river below C. The sewage treatment plant had primary and secondary treatment systems and a chlorinated effluent.

In Table 4-1 are shown results of tests at the five stations marked on the map. Can you see some of the effects that the effluents from the industrial plants and the sewage treatment works had on the river in 1965?

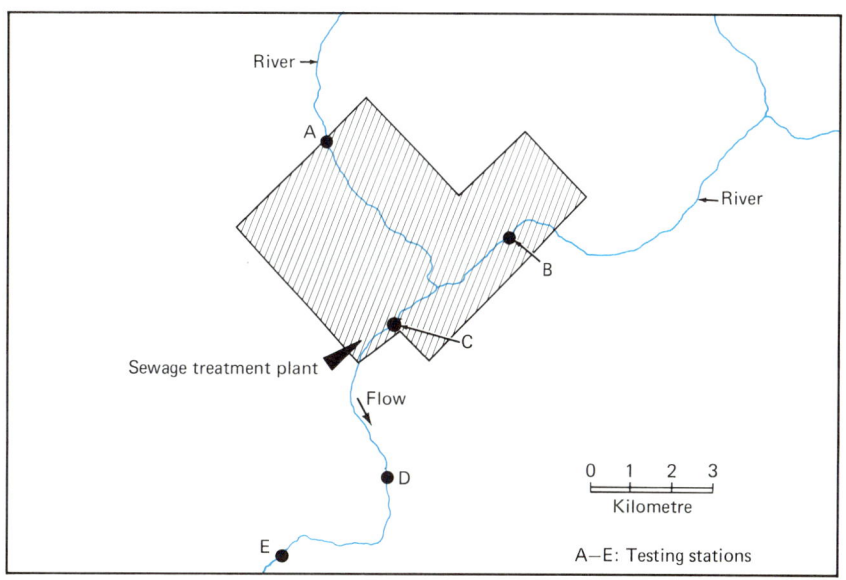

Figure 4-4. Map showing the testing stations.

			Total solids (TSS + TDS) in ppm			Total coliforms (per 100 cm³)	Dissolved oxygen in ppm			
Date	Testing Station	B.O.D. in ppm		Nitrogen in ppm	Phosphorus in ppm		Max.	Min.	Total fish	Number of organisms
1965	A	1.6	286	0.71	0.16	1 875	N.S.	N.S.	129	260
1970		0.5	300	0.63	0.029	410	N.S.	N.S.	387	100
1965	B	7.0	412	1.80	3.10	180 075	12.0	7.0	493	100
1970		1.8	362	0.62	0.028	1 500	12.0	7.0	215	10
1965	C	3.7	418	1.50	0.95	32 175	10.0	5.0	177	180
1970		1.6	367	0.71	0.044	1 000	14.0	7.0	110	25
1965	D	8.7	493	2.70	1.92	1 283	5.0	1.0	2	300
1970		4.7	431	2.15	0.33	460	6.0	1.5	0	1335
1965	E	3.0	503	1.30	1.60	N.S.	N.S.	N.S.	3	900
1970		4.7	415	0.88	0.24	N.S.	N.S.	N.S.	28	350

Table 4-1 RESULTS OF TESTS ON RIVER

N.S. *Not sampled*

Five years later two companies had stopped operating in the city and others had re-routed their wastes through the sewage treatment plant. The capacity of the plant had been increased, and improved equipment (to remove phosphorus) was going to be installed.

Results of re-tests made in 1970 are also shown in Table 4-1. In what ways had the quality of the water apparently improved or worsened? Here are some clues.

Chemical characteristics. Only about 50% of the nitrogen and 55% of the phosphorus is removed by primary and secondary sewage treatment. Concentrations of 0.3 ppm nitrogen and 0.01 ppm phosphorus will give an algae bloom.

Coliforms. The lower the coliform count, the lower is the level of bacterial polution. This finding came from using the coliform test (Experiment 3.9).

If the *dissolved oxygen content* is less than 5 ppm and the B.O.D. greater than 5 ppm, then the sample is considered to be polluted.

Fish. Usually the fewer the fish, the more polluted is the water. Chlorination tends to kill fish or drive them away.

Organisms. In general, the fewer the organisms, the less polluted is the sample. However, there will always be some organisms unless the water is toxic. At D in 1970, 1 300 of the 1 335 organisms were sludgeworms, a pollution-resistant species.

The tests shown in Table 4-1 were made in May of each year. Some were repeated at other times of the year so that comparisons could be made. It is unwise to try to reach firm conclusions about the health of a river from tests made in one season only. A long dry spell, for instance, or a late Spring runoff could affect the results abnormally.

5

Sewage and water treatment

Sewage treatment

Sewage treatment is intended to remove contaminants from used water before it enters waterways. There are three stages of treatment: primary, secondary and tertiary.

Primary

In primary treatment the sewage passes through a screen which traps large solids; dust and grit particles are allowed to settle; scum is skimmed from the surface. This process removes 60 per cent of the solids and 35 per cent of the B.O.D. The solids that accumulate can be purified and used as landfill.

Secondary

Secondary treatment (Figures 5-1 or 5-2) treats the sewage remaining after primary treatment. Bacteria added to the sewage act as decomposers in breaking down carbohydrates and proteins into simpler products such as carbon dioxide and nitrates. While feeding on these nutrients, they use up the dissolved oxygen in their metabolic processes. Aeration is therefore necessary to replace the oxygen and keep the bacteria at work. The resulting liquor is 90 per cent free of suspended solids and has 95 per cent of the B.O.D. removed. Next it is chlorinated to kill the bacteria. It is then discharged into the waterways or treated in the tertiary stage.

The solids removed by the primary and secondary treatment are usually rich in nutrients and can be made into fertilizer. They can also be 'digested' by bacteria. This process produces combustible gases which can be used for fuel to help run the sewage treatment plant.

Figure 5-1 (below). Typical aeration equipment for secondary sewage treatment.

Figure 5-2 (below right). The large round pieces of equipment in the middle of the photograph are trickle filter beds sometimes used in secondary sewage treatment. The sewage passes through the rotating 'arms' and drops into the filter beds.

50 ppm NO_3^- in drinking water can cause a cyanotic condition, similar in appearance to the 'blue-baby' syndrome.

Primary and secondary treatment removes only some of the soluble materials. These include nitrate ions, phosphate ions, chloride ions, sodium ions, and potassium ions. Nitrates and phosphates and the results of discharging them into waterways were discussed in Chapter 3. Fixed nitrogen and precious non-renewable phosphates, instead of being completely recycled, continue to pollute our water resources.

Tertiary treatment is intended to remove phosphates and nitrates from sewage. Can you suggest how? Maybe a review of Chapter 2 will give you some ideas.

Experiment 5.1
Precipitation of phosphates

Dissolve a few grams of sodium phosphate (trisodium tetraoxophosphate) in water. Add calcium hydroxide solution (lime water). What do you see? What precipitate has been produced?

$$\text{calcium hydroxide} + \text{sodium phosphate} \longrightarrow \text{calcium phosphate} + \text{sodium hydroxide}$$

$$3Ca(OH)_2 + 2Na_3PO_4 \longrightarrow Ca_3(PO_4)_2 + 6NaOH$$

$$3Ca^{2+}(aq) + 6OH^-(aq) + 6Na^+(aq) + 2PO_4^{3-}(aq) \longrightarrow Ca_3^{2+}(PO_4^{3-})_2(s) + 6Na^+(aq) + 6OH^-(aq)$$

This is one method that can be used to rid sewage of phosphates. Would a similar method work for nitrates? Justify your answer.

Most sewage treatment plants have no tertiary stage. Some Canadian municipalities do not even have a primary treatment plant.

Lagoon method

In some rural areas, household wastes are piped or dumped into a 'lagoon', or large artificial pond. These wastes stimulate the growth of algae that produce oxygen through photosynthesis. Bacteria, snails and worms use the oxygen to break down the organic material. If the pond is stocked with fish (carp have been used), they feed on plants whose growth is encouraged by human wastes; and if we eat the fish the ecological cycle is complete. A sophisticated version of this method is now being perfected in Japan.

The lagoon method is slow and uses a large area. It can be suitable for small townships but not for big cities. Moreover it can create problems in winter if the lagoon freezes.

Industrial effluent control

Industry is responsible for treating its own effluent. In Chapter 4 industrial pollutants were discussed. Some of these are poisonous and, if discharged through the municipal sewage system, could poison the bacteria in the secondary stage of treatment.

The ions of silver, copper and chromium, which are common industrial pollutants, are very toxic to fish. As little as 0.03 ppm Cu^{2+} is fatal to some species of trout. Poisons can kill bacteria in water and also hinder the growth of algae. At times water is literally lifeless.

Industry could very well control most of its effluents. It is mainly economic factors that make some companies reluctant to do so. Informed public opinion is extremely valuable in convincing industry of the need to maintain a natural ecological balance.

Treatment of drinking water

The treatment of drinking water consists basically of filtration and chlorination. The first process gets rid of large particles; the second kills bacteria.

Experiment 5.2
Flocculation

Take a 250 cm^3 measuring cylinder and add 200 cm^3 of water and a few spoonsfull of soil. Shake the cylinder well and let the contents settle. Is the water clear? Add a few grams of alum (potassium aluminium sulfate); shake and allow the contents to settle again. Is the water any clearer?

Repeat the experiment, this time filtering the soil solution first. Is the filtrate clear? Add alum to the filtrate, shake and allow it to stand. Does it become clear?

This second procedure is called *flocculation*. It is used in water treatment plants to clear the water of soil and silt particles.

Experiment 5.3
Adsorption on charcoal

Use rubber gloves and a fume hood for this experiment because bromine can cause serious burns and its fumes are harmful. The used charcoal can be disposed of by adding it to a large amount (500 cm^3) of dilute ammonium solution (0.2 mol·dm^{-3}).

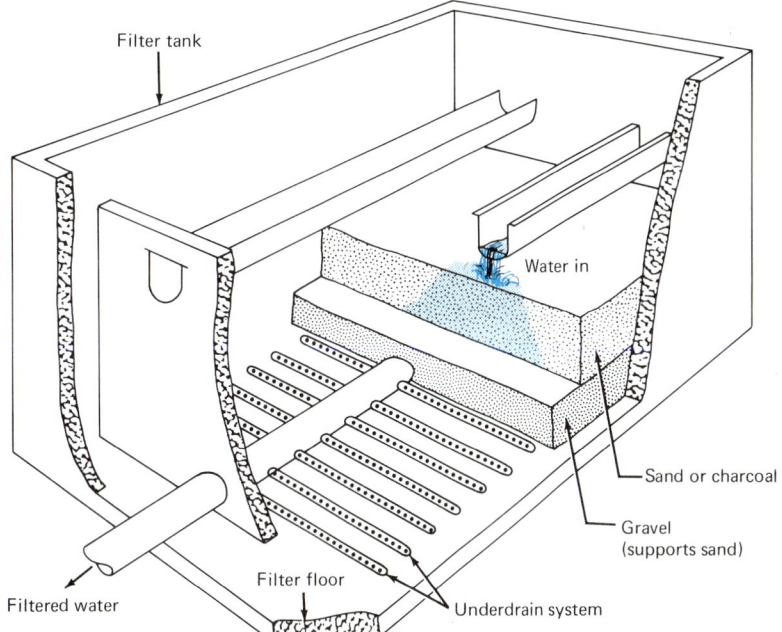

Figure 5-3. A filtering system for purifying water. Partially treated water passes through the sand and gravel, and then through the under-drains into a clean-water reservoir. Along the way, the impurities are trapped. By reversing the water flow, the system is cleaned of accumulated wastes at regular intervals.

Add a few drops of bromine to a large flask and insert a stopper. When the flask is full of bromine vapour, add a few teaspoonsful of activated charcoal. Replace the stopper and shake the flask. What do you see happening?

Make a pale purple solution of potassium manganate(VII). Pass this through a filter of activated charcoal. What colour is the filtered solution? Activated charcoal can adsorb a large number and quantity of chemicals. *Adsorption* is the attraction between molecules of gases or solutions and the surface molecules of solids.

Experiment 5.4
Chlorination

It is possible to see bacteria in stagnant water through a microscope. Examine a sample; then add some chlorine water or calcium hypochlorite (chlorinated lime, or bleaching powder) and examine again. Are there any bacteria left alive?

Figure 5-4 (right). Distillation apparatus for Experiment 5.5.

Figure 5-5 (below). This graph shows the dramatic reduction in the North American death rate from typhoid (a water-borne disease) after the chlorination of domestic water supplies was introduced in 1908.

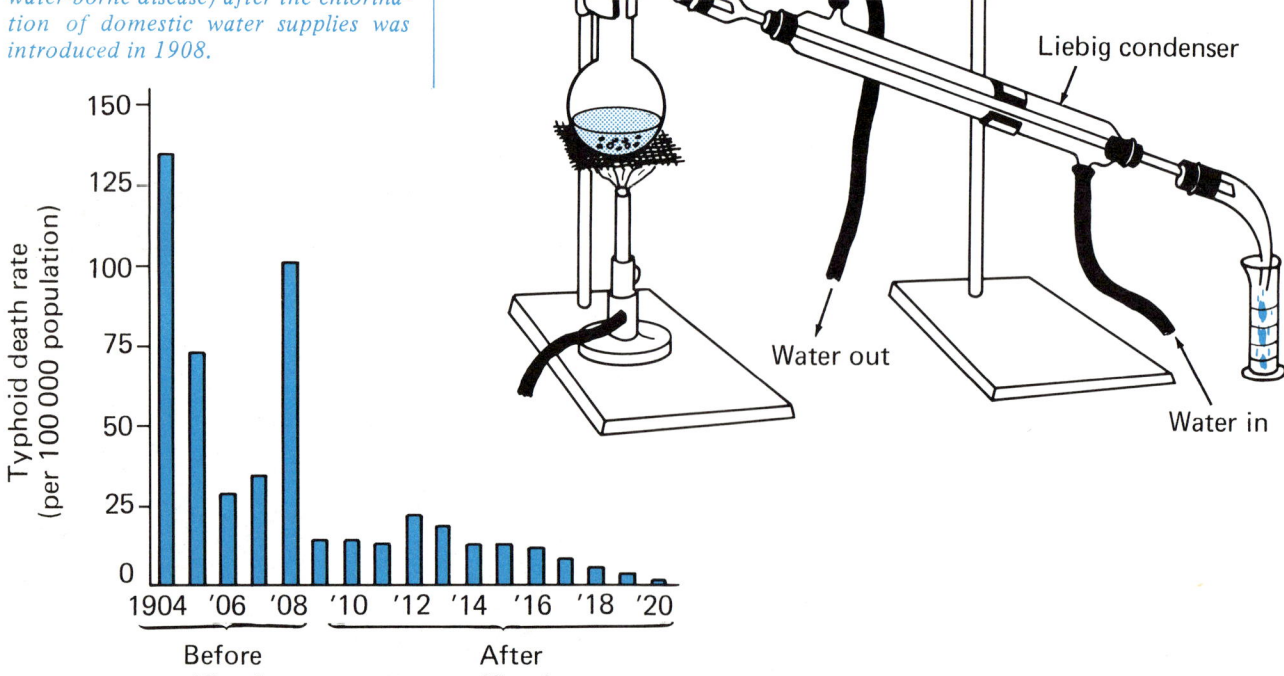

Some particles that are soluble in water, such as nitrate, phosphate (PO_4^{3-}) and chloride ions, are not all trapped by flocculation and filtration. As a result these particles increase in concentration. The acceptable limit of concentration for nitrates is 10 ppm. Other ions little affected by water treatment are arsenic, cadmium, chromium, copper, fluoride, and lead.

Set up the apparatus as shown in Figure 5-4. Turn on the tap and let cold water circulate through the Liebig condenser. Add salt water to the flask and boil it. At what temperature does the solution boil? Collect the product and taste it. Is it salty? Find the boiling point of this product. Compare it to that of the salt solution?

If you drink too much salt water you will die: many a sailor has perished of thirst while surrounded by water. Distillation is the easiest way to desalinate water on a small scale. Other methods are ion exchange and dialysis which are expensive and therefore not very practical. A lot of research is being done to find a cheap, practical, large-scale method of desalination.

Experiment 5.5
Distillation of salt water

Summary

Sewage treatment
Primary: Removes solids.
Secondary: Removes organic matter.
Tertiary: Removes nitrates and phosphates.

Water treatment
Flocculation: Removes most suspended solids.
Filtration: Removes most dissolved solids.
Chlorination: Kills bacteria and viruses.

In 1831 sewage outlet pipes to the Thames River in London England were upstream from the inlet pipes to water companies. A cholera epidemic which killed about 50 000 people occurred in the city in that year.

Concentration of some chemicals in sea water (kilograms per cubic metre): NaCl, 27.2; $MgCl_2$, 3.8; $MgSO_4$, 1.7; $CaSO_4$, 1.3; K_2SO_4, 0.9.

Solar distillation by the 'flash' method costs approximately 26 cents per cubic metre of fresh water produced. Normal, non-solar methods cost about 4¾ cents per cubic metre.

Figure 5-6. A solar 'flash' desalination plant at Eilat, Israel: capacity 3800m³ per day.

6

The physics and chemistry of water

Liquid and solid

Although water is the commonest liquid on earth — it covers 71 per cent of the earth's surface — it is one of the oddest liquids known. By comparing water with other liquids, we can learn something about its strange behaviour.

Experiment 6.1
Floating properties

Put some 1,4-dichlorobenzene (paradichlorobenzene) crystals to a depth of about 5 cm in a long test tube. Heat the contents in a water-bath until they are liquid. Drop some more crystals of 1,4-dichlorobenzene into the molten liquid. Do they float or sink before melting? Compare this with ice and water.

Water is one of the few liquids that can float its own solid. Look up the densities of some other chemicals in their liquid and solid states and determine whether or not the solid will float in the liquid. There are only a few other solids that float in their own liquid. Among these are the metals bismuth and antimony. Try to imagine what would happen to water plants and animals if ice did not float.

Experiment 6.2
Freezing point of water

Take a beaker partly filled with cold water and add ice cubes until their volume is greater than the volume of the water. A few minutes later stir; then take the temperature of the water. Repeat the readings until they remain constant.

Now add a few grams of sodium chloride crystals and stir. Take the temperature again. What effect has the salt had on the freezing temperature of the water? Explain from this why salt is sprinkled on roads in winter.

Experiment 6.3
Boiling point of water

Heat a beaker half-full of water until it boils. Take the temperature of the boiling water. Add a few grams of sodium chloride crystals to the boiling water and retake the temperature. Again add a few grams of sodium chloride and read off the temperature. Compare the three temperature readings of the boiling water.

Continue the boiling in the open beaker for about 10 minutes, reading the temperature every minute. What happens? Why?

Boiling point of water and other liquids

How does the boiling point of water compare with that of other substances?

It would appear that the heavier the molecule, the higher the boiling

Table 6-1 BOILING POINTS OF ALCOHOLS ($^{\circ}$C)				
	Methanol	Ethanol	Propan-1-ol	Butan-1-ol
Formula	CH_3OH	C_2H_5OH	C_3H_7OH	C_4H_9OH
Boiling point	64.7	78	97	117
Molecular mass	32	46	60	74

point; yet the boiling points of methanol, ethanol and propan-1-ol are less than that of water, even though they are heavier molecules.

Table 6-2 BOILING POINTS OF GROUP VI HYDRIDES ($^\circ$C)				
	(Di)hydrogen oxide (water)	(Di)hydrogen sulfide	(Di)hydrogen selenide	(Di)hydrogen telluride
Formula	H_2O	H_2S	H_2Se	H_2Te
Boiling point	100	−59.6	−41.5	−2
Molecular mass	18	34	81	130

The same trend is followed in Table 6-2 as in Table 6-1. The heavier the molecule, the higher is the boiling point — except for water! Is this trend repeated with other groups in the periodic table?

Table 6-3 BOILING POINTS OF HALOGEN HYDRIDES ($^\circ$C)				
	Hydrogen fluoride	Hydrogen chloride	Hydrogen bromide	Hydrogen iodide
Formula	HF	HCl	HBr	HI
Boiling point	19.6	−85.0	−69	−36
Molecular mass	20	36.5	81	128

Table 6-4 BOILING POINTS OF GROUP V HYDRIDES ($^\circ$C)				
	Ammonia	Phosphine	Arsine	Stibine
Formula	NH_3	PH_3	AsH_3	SbH_3
Boiling point	−33.3	−87.4	−55	−17
Molecular Mass	17	34	78	125

Tables 6-3 and 6-4 show the same trend as Table 6-2. The first member of each group is the exception. It seems probable that a table of group IV hydrides would show the same pattern.

Table 6-5 BOILING POINTS OF GROUP IV HYDRIDES ($^\circ$C)				
	Methane	Silane	Germanium (tetra)hydride	Tin (tetra)hydride
Formula	CH_4	SiH_4	GeH_4	SnH_4
Boiling point	−161	−112	−88.5	−52
Molecular mass	16	32	77	123

This time the trend is not followed. Table 6-5 is similar to Table 6-1.

Methane is not an exception. Let us consider the three exceptions, hydrogen fluoride, water and ammonia.

Table 6-6 BOILING POINTS OF 'ODD' SUBSTANCES (°C)			
	Ammonia	Water	Hydrogen fluoride
Formula	NH_3	H_2O	HF
Boiling Point	−33.3	100	19.6
Molecular mass	17	18	20

Even among the compounds with anomalously high boiling points, water has by far the highest! Even the fact that water is a liquid under normal conditions makes it exceptional. If it had followed the pattern of Table 6-2, it would have been a gas at standard temperature and pressure. Tables 6-2 through 6-6 are summarized in Figure 6-1.

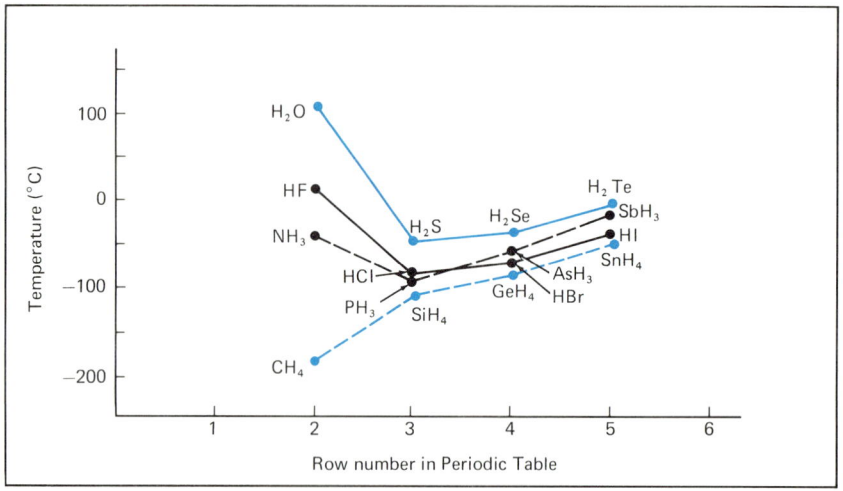

Figure 6-1. (below right). The graph shows the boiling points of the hydrides in Tables 6-2 through 6-6. The 'normal' trend is shown by the bottom blue line. The boiling point increases with increasing molecular mass. In the other three series, the first members have a surprisingly high boiling point.

Figure 6-2 (below). Water boiling in an evacuated chamber.

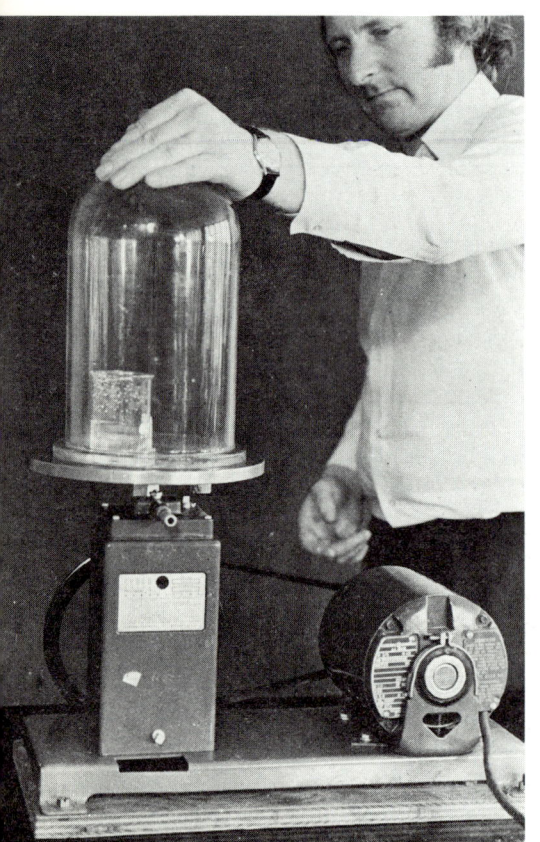

Look up the temperature at which water will boil 500 metres down a mine shaft, or in a chalet 3000 metres up a mountain. What causes these changes? At what temperature do you think water will boil in a pressure cooker? As a teacher demonstration, a beaker of water could be placed in a bell jar evacuated by a vacuum pump. At what temperature does the water boil? (See Figure 6-2.)

Forces between molecules

Experiment 6.4
Solubility and insolubility

In water, glass is more soluble than tin.

Add a few crystals of sodium chloride to a test tube half-full of distilled water. Shake the tube. Does the solid dissolve?

Repeat the experiment with lead chloride. Does it dissolve? Why does one salt dissolve and another one not?

Note: tetrachloromethane (carbon tetrachloride) fumes are dangerous. Parts of Experiments 6.5, 6.6, 6.7, 6.8 and 6.9 should be carried out under a fume hood. Wear rubber gloves to avoid contact with the liquid.

Experiment 6.5
Will it mix?

To a test tube one-third full of water, add an equal amount of ethanol (ethyl alcohol). Shake the tube. Do the two liquids mix? Repeat the experiment using tetrachloromethane. Does mixing occur this time? Why do the liquids mix in one case, but not in the other?

Experiment 6.6
A water 'sandwich'

Take 4 clean test tubes. Add $10 \, cm^3$ of water to two of them and $10 \, cm^3$ of tetrachloromethane to the other two. Add a crystal of solid iodine to one sample of each liquid and a crystal of potassium manganate(VII) to the other sample of each liquid.

Why does dissolving occur in two tubes, but not in the other two?

Slowly add the contents of the water-and-iodine test tube to the tetrachloromethane-and-iodine test tube. In a new test tube add one crystal of iodine to $10 \, cm^3$ of kerosene and pour this solution slowly into the mixture you have just made.

Try to devise an experiment to produce a purple liquid between two clear liquids.

Iodine is a non-polar solid; potassium manganate(VII) is an ionic, and therefore polar, solid. In aqueous solution, therefore, iodine is similar in behaviour to tetrachloromethane; potassium manganate(VII) is similar in behaviour to sodium chloride which dissolves readily in water.

To understand Experiments 6.4, 6.5 and 6.6, you need to know about a special property of water molecules. You should be able to find out what this is from the next two experiments.

Experiment 6.7
'Walking on water'

Fill a beaker with water and try to float a small pin on the surface. Repeat the experiment with tetrachloromethane, placing the pin on the surface with forceps. Will supporting the pin on a piece of filter paper help?

How can steel (density $7\,800 \, g \cdot dm^{-3}$) float on water (density $1\,000 \, g \cdot dm^{-3}$) but not on tetrachloromethane (density $1\,600 \, g \cdot dm^{-3}$)?

Experiment 6.8
Drops: round or not?

Sketch the shape of a drop of water just before it leaves the end of an eye dropper. Do the same for tetrachloromethane.

Fill a long test tube with castor oil, whose density is just less than $1000 \text{ g} \cdot \text{dm}^{-3}$. Sketch the shape of a drop of water as it falls through the oil. Repeat, using tetrachloromethane falling through water.

One interpretation of Experiments 6.7 and 6.8 is that water molecules are strongly attracted to one another. Energy is needed to break this attraction. This would explain why the light pin does not break the surface of the water, and why the shape of the drop is spherical. (The smallest volume contained by any given surface is a sphere.) What causes this attraction?

Experiment 6.9
Water as a 'magnet'

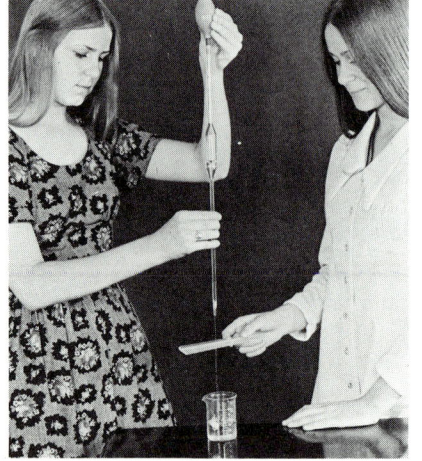

Fill a 25 cm³ pipette with water. Rub a plastic comb on a woollen garment or through your hair, or rub an ebonite rod with fur. Let the water run out of the pipette and hold the comb or rod close to it, as in Figure 6.3. What happens? Repeat the experiment using first ethanol and then tetrachloromethane. Use a pipette with a rubber bulb to draw up 25 cm³ of each of these liquids.

Try to repel the stream of water. (Think about your studies in electrostatics.)

Figure 6-3. Procedure for the water part of Experiment 6.9.

The secret is that the water molecule is polar. Water molecules *act like* small 'magnets' attracting one another.

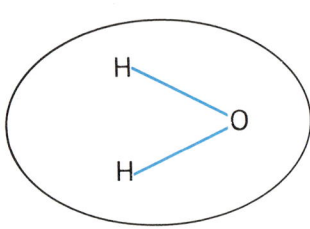

A molecule of water.

If your comb was positively charged, then:

but if your comb was negatively charged, then:

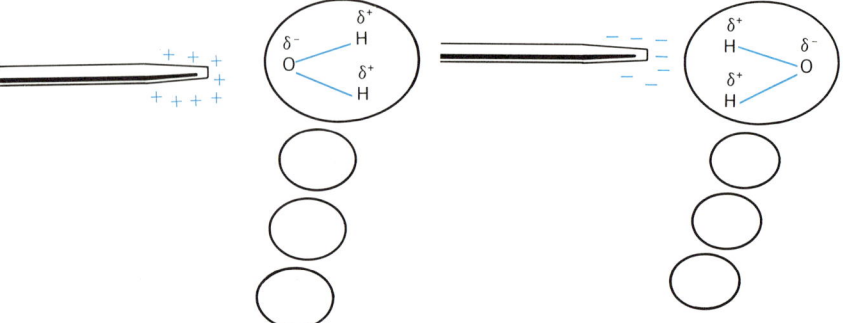

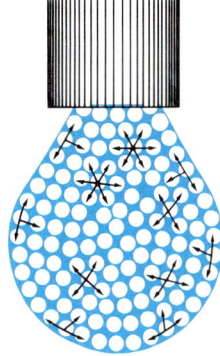

Figure 6-4 (above). A drop of water. The direction of the forces of attraction is shown by the arrows. The drop is not completely spherical until it leaves the tap.

Figure 6-5 (right). The addition of detergent lessens the surface tension of the water, and the drop spreads over a larger area than it would otherwise have done.

Figure 6-6.(a) The tetrachloromethane molecules cannot get in between the water molecules. This prevents the two liquids from mixing. Why is the tetrachloromethane underneath? (b) Water and ethanol molecules mix freely because both are polar covalent and so attract one another. The molecules are always moving and forces of attraction and repulsion are always at work.

Therefore no matter what you tried, the water would have been attracted.

The ethanol (alcohol) molecule is also polar, but not as strongly as water. The tetrachloromethane molecule is non-polar.

In Experiment 6.6 the attraction of the water molecules for one another did not allow the pin to sink. The pin would first have had to break the 'skin' on the surface of the water; that is, it would have had to break the mutual attraction of the water molecules directly beneath it. This property, which also allows mosquitoes and other insects to walk on water, is called surface tension.

If every water molecule is attracted to every other water molecule, they must pack together as closely as possible. This produces a spherical shape, as in Figure 6-4.

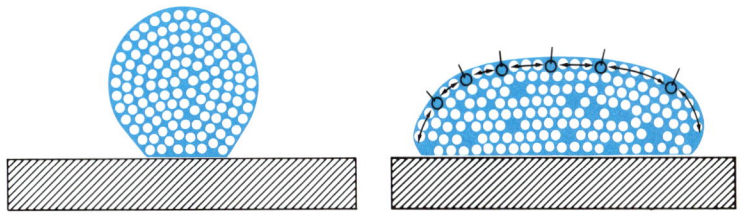

This property of water is often a nuisance. For instance, water will not completely wet glass or your skin. Detergent molecules (see Chapter 2) break down this attraction and lessen the surface tension. The water therefore covers a greater area. This is shown in Figure 6-5.

In Experiment 6.5, the water and tetrachloromethane did not mix because the tetrachloromethane, being non-polar, could not break the attraction between the water molecules. Ethanol, like water, is polar and its molecules can attract water molecules, just as water molecules can attract ethanol molecules. Mixing was therefore possible. (See Figure 6-6.)

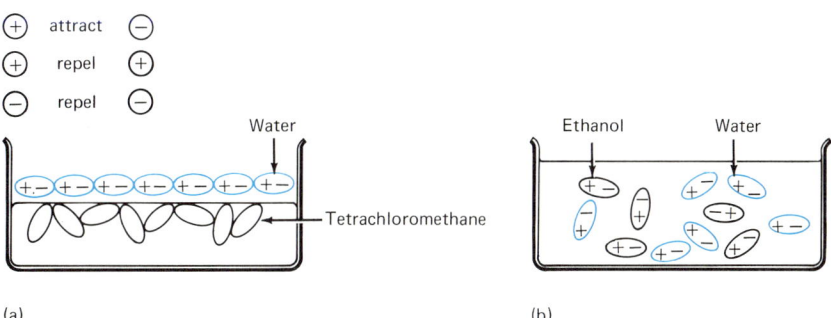

If water and ethanol are not stirred, two layers can be observed. This shows that the attraction between water molecules is strong; stirring is needed for the two layers to mix.

'Magnets' and 'magnetic' have been placed in quotation marks because the water molecule is not actually magnetic. The attraction of the water molecule for the charged rod is electrostatic. The words have been used merely to give an idea of the way in which water behaves.

Would a thin stream of water be deflected by a bar magnet?

Polar covalency in water

Figure 6-7 (right). This diagram of a water molecule shows its polar nature (b).

(a) (b)

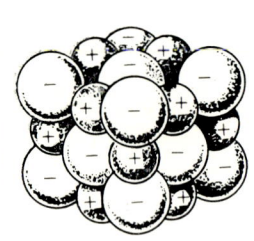

Figure 6-8 (above). This is part of a sodium chloride crystal lattice. An actual crystal of sodium chloride has this basic structure extended in three dimensions. 1 g of Na^+Cl^- would contain approximately 10^{22} ions.

In Figure 6-7 (a), each line joining a hydrogen and oxygen atom represents a shared pair of electrons. Are these electrons equally or unequally shared? Which atom will attract the electrons more, the hydrogen (with one proton) or the oxygen (with eight protons)? As one might expect, oxygen will attract the shared pair of electrons more than hydrogen because it has a greater attraction for electrons than hydrogen, that is, a greater electronegativity. Because of this unequal sharing, the bond is said to be *polar covalent*. (See *Action Chemistry* p. 55.)

In Figure 6-7 (b), the Greek letter delta (δ) shows that the electrons are not completly transferred as they are in Na^+Cl^-, but are unequally shared. (δ in mathematics means *a little bit*.) This unequal sharing is the reason for water's 'magnetic' properties.

Solubility and insolubility

A crystal of sodium chloride has the structure shown in Figure 6-8. The water molecule, being polar, is attracted to the ions. (See Figure 6-9 (a).) If the surface ions are more attracted to the water molecules than they are to the rest of the lattice, then the solid will dissolve. The resulting particles are shown in Figure 6-9 (b). If the opposite is true, the solid will be insoluble, as with lead chloride. (Experiment 6.4.)

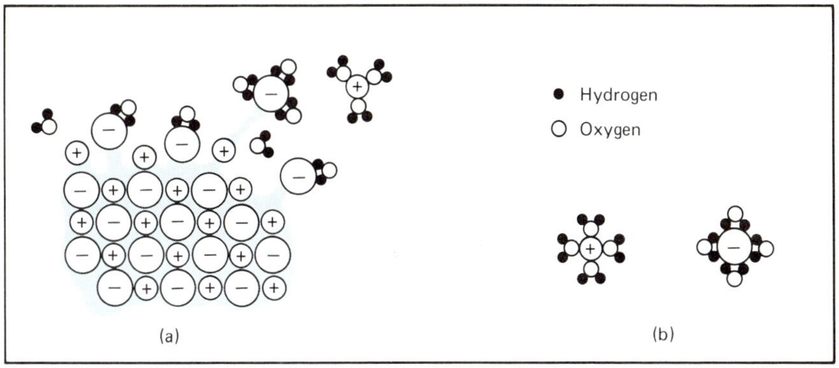

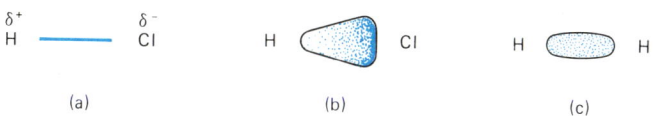

Figure 6-9. (a) Sodium chloride dissolving in water. (b) Particles present in a solution of sodium chloride.

Experiment 6.10
Properties of sulfuric acid

Warning: concentrated sulfuric acid is a very dangerous chemical and you should perform this experiment only with permission from your teacher.

Take a piece of blue litmus paper. Moisten half with water, keeping the other half dry. Dry the moist half on filter paper. Use forceps to place the litmus paper on the surface of a small beaker of concentrated sulfuric acid. Compare the effect on both halves of the paper.

Why did only half of the litmus paper turn red? (The reason the paper disintegrated almost immediately is another matter altogether!)

Litmus paper will turn red in the presence of hydrated hydrogen ions ($H^+ \cdot n H_2 O$). Pure hydrogen sulfate ($H_2 SO_4$) contains no hydrogen ions, but, when it is dissolved in water, hydrogen ions are produced in large quantities, and sulfuric acid is formed.

Pure hydrogen nitrate (HNO_3) and pure hydrogen chloride (HCl) are covalent compounds. They are not the type of substances you would immediately identify as acids, but when dissolved in water they produce nitric acid and hydrochloric acid and exhibit the acid properties you are familiar with.

Figure 6-10. (a) represents a molecule of hydrogen chloride and shows that the hydrogen atom is slightly positively charged and the chlorine atom slightly negatively charged. (b) also represents an HCl molecule. (c) represents a molecule of hydrogen gas (H_2) and shows how the pair of bonding electrons are equally shared between the two hydrogen atoms; this makes the molecule non-polar covalent. (b) is polar covalent because the pair of bonding electrons is unequally shared: that is, the bonding electrons spend more than 50 per cent of the time closer to the chlorine atom. It is this which accounts for the slight negative charge on the chlorine end of the molecule and the slight positive charge on the hydrogen end.

$$\overset{\delta^+}{H} \text{———} \overset{\delta^-}{Cl} \qquad H \quad Cl \qquad H \quad H$$

(a)   (b)   (c)

As is shown in Figure 6-10, the hydrogen chloride molecule is diatomic (two atoms) and polar covalent in a similar way to the water molecule. The negative ends of water molecules and the positive ends of hydrogen chloride molecules will attract each other; in the same way, the positive ends of water molecules and the negative ends of hydrogen chloride molecules will attract each other; and a tug-of-war begins. The water molecules win; that is, they succeed in pulling hydrogen chloride molecules apart. (Figure 6-11).

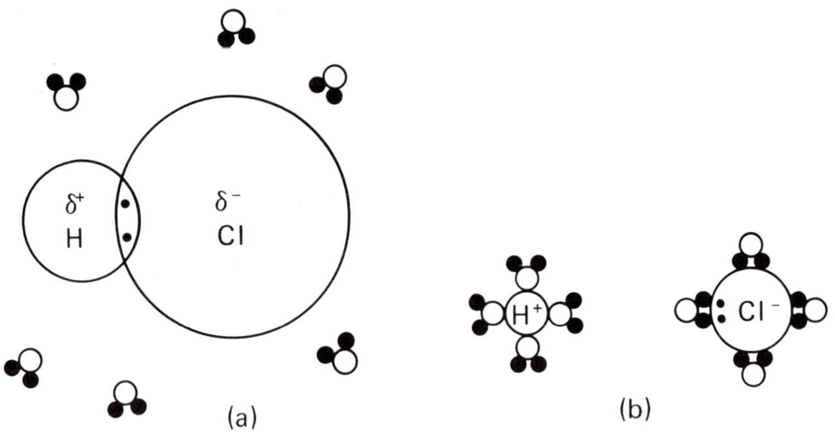

Figure 6-11. These diagrams show how hydrogen chloride gas dissolves in water. In (a), water molecules approach the hydrogen chloride molecule. (The molecules are always moving.) (b) shows the final aquated (hydrated) ions.

The same process occurs with the H_2SO_4 and HNO_3 molecules.

$$H_2SO_4 (l) + nH_2O (l) \longrightarrow 2H^+(aq) + SO_4^{2-}(aq)$$

Effects of heating water

Table 6-7 COMPARISON OF WATER AND TETRACHLOROMETHANE			
	Units	Water	Tetrachloro-methane
Molecular mass		18.016	153.823
Boiling point	°C	100.00	76.8
Melting point	°C	0.00	−22.9
Maximum density	$kg \cdot m^{-3}$	1 000.000	
Temp. of maximum density	°C	3.98	
Specific heat capacity at 3.98°C	$kJ \cdot (kg \cdot K)^{-1}$	4.205	0.84
Molar heat of vaporization	$kJ \cdot mol^{-1}$	40.651	20.9
Molar heat of fusion (melting)	$kJ \cdot mol^{-1}$	6.010	2.5
Surface tension	$N \cdot m^{-1}$	0.072	0.027

In Table 6-7 the values for water are higher, even though its molecular mass is less than that of tetrachloromethane. These values show that it is relatively difficult to move and separate water molecules. This is because of the type of attraction water molecules have for one another. For instance, it takes relatively more heat to raise a given number of water molecules through 1°C than it does to raise the same number of tetrachloromethane molecules through 1°C. The water molecules, though each of smaller mass, are harder to move.

Similarly, more energy is needed to change water at 100°C into steam than to change tetrachloromethane liquid at 77°C into its vapour. Again, water molecules are more difficult to separate.

The practical applications of the properties of water include the following.

(a) The specific heats of rock and soil are lower than that of water, so that the same amount of heat will raise the temperature of land more than that of water. This explains land and sea breezes: when warmed air over the land rises, cooler air is drawn in from over the water. The pattern is often the opposite at night, as land cools down more quickly than water. For this reason seas and oceans moderate the climate of many countries. Compare the climates of the following cities which are at roughly the same latitude: Glasgow in Scotland, Moscow and Novosibirsk in the U.S.S.R., and Edmonton and Prince Rupert in Canada.

(b) Water has a high heat of vaporization. This means that when a little water evaporates a large amount of heat is lost. When we perspire, our body loses a small amount of water compared to the heat lost in its evaporation.

Water vapour forms above a large mass of water; if a wind blows this vapour away, more water will evaporate to maintain the equilibrium. The heat needed for this evaporation can only come from the water itself and hence its temperature will fall.

(c) When water freezes, it gives out a lot of heat. This is one of the reasons why a wine industry is located along the shores of Lake Ontario on the Niagara Peninsula. In winter, cold temperatures freeze in-shore water, which gives out heat and helps to prevent the vines from being damaged. Farther out the water remains unfrozen, and this large body of water moderates the climate, as was explained in (a) above. In spring the ice melts. Melting absorbs a lot of heat and therefore helps to prevent prematurely high temperatures.

If cooled slowly and carefully enough under certain conditions, absolutely pure water will remain a liquid down to a temperature of −42°C.

Hydrogen bonding

Polar covalent molecules (e.g. HCl) attract one another because of their slight positive and negative charges. Of these, ammonia (NH_3), hydrogen fluoride (HF) and water (H_2O), among the chemicals in Figure 6-2, show this attraction much more strongly than the others. This accounts for their abnormally high melting points and boiling points. The strong forces of attraction between these molecules are called *hydrogen bonds*. (Hydrogen bonds should not be confused with the bonds within the molecules themselves.)

Of these three compounds, water is unique. Hydrogen bonding between water molecules is exceptionally strong, so that water displays the characteristics of hydrogen bonding to a much greater degree. Without hydrogen bonding, water would boil somewhere below −50°C! However, hydrogen bonds, even in water, are still much weaker than the bonds that hold atoms together in a molecule.

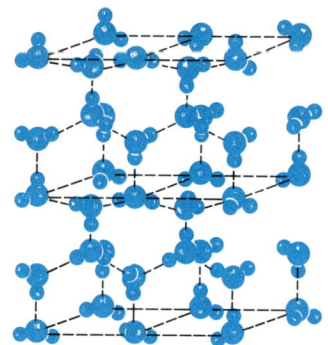

Figure 6-12. *This is a diagram of an ice crystal. The small atoms are hydrogen and the larger ones oxygen. The attraction is between the hydrogen atoms of one molecule and the oxygen atoms of adjacent molecules. When ice melts, the H_2O molecules come closer together and only start to move apart at $4°C$.*

Hydrogen bonding is at its maximum in ice, where almost all the molecules are hydrogen bonded and form a solid, ordered, crystal-lattice structure in which they are held much farther apart than in the liquid state. (See Figure 6-12.) The heat which melts the ice breaks many of the hydrogen bonds and reduces the crystal structure of the ice to hydrogen-bonded liquid 'fragments'. At this point ($0°C - 0.01°C$) as the ice turns to water, there is a pronounced decrease in volume (increase in density) of H_2O. (See Figure 6-13.) As the heating continues, all the ice melts and the water begins to rise in temperature. While this is happening, more and more hydrogen bonds are broken. The molecules pack closer together so that the density of the water is increased even more. From $0°C$ to $4°C$, this breaking of hydrogen bonds and consequent *increase in density* prevails over the other effect of the heat, which is, to increase molecular motion and so *decrease density*. That is the reason why there is a *net increase* in the density of water between these temperatures. At $4°C$ ($3.98°C$ exactly) water is at its maximum density. At $4°C$, the increased kinetic energy of the molecules begins to prevail over their tendency to draw closer together. Therefore, at $4°C$ the density of water begins to decrease and goes on decreasing as its temperature rises. Hydrogen bonding persists in its effect, however, and accounts for most of liquid water's unique and unusual properties. Even in water vapour, a very few molecules at a time continue to form, break and re-form hydrogen bonds.

It is fortunate indeed for life on Earth that water, unlike most other liquids, reaches its maximum density *before* it freezes. Otherwise, since denser liquids sink in less dense ones, water cooled to the freezing point would sink to the bottom of lakes and oceans, and permanent ice would form from the bottom up!

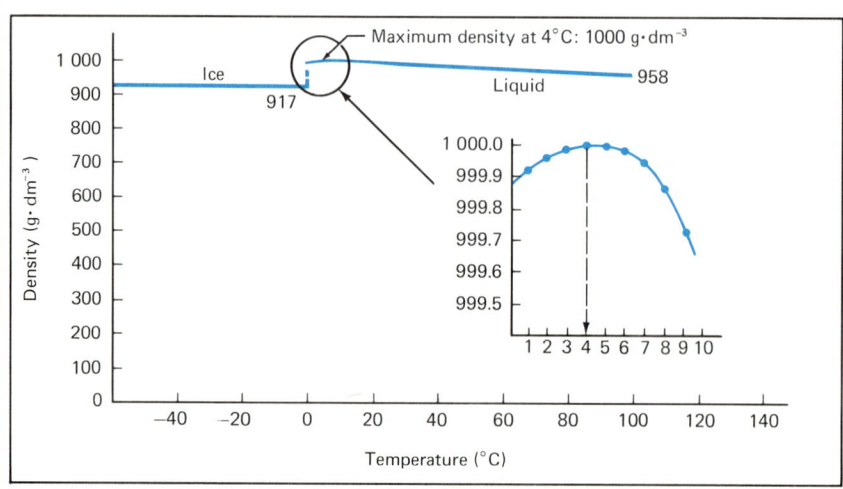

Figure 6-13. *Density of water at various temperatures.*

Heavy water

Heavy hydrogen consists of one proton, one neutron and one electron. It therefore has double the mass of ordinary hydrogen. Heavy hydrogen is an isotope of hydrogen, called deuterium (D). Heavy water has the formula D_2O and has similar properties to H_2O.

Heavy water is very important to Canada's nuclear power program since it has been chosen as the moderator in CANDU nuclear reactors. (See Figure 4-1, page 29.) Because of its scarcity in normal water (only 1 part in 7 000), heavy water is difficult to extract and isolate. In practice, roughly 450 000 litres of ordinary water are needed to produce 1 litre of heavy water.

Hydrogen consists of three isotopes: $_1^1H$, $_1^2H$, and $_1^3H$, of which $_1^1H$ is by far the most common.

Oxygen consists of three isotopes: $_8^{16}O$, $_8^{17}O$, and $_8^{18}O$, of which $_8^{16}O$ is by far the most common.

There are, therefore, 18 different types of water molecule, of which $_1^1H_2{}_8^{16}O$ is by far the most common.

Table 6-8 PHYSICAL PROPERTIES OF WATER (H_2O) AND HEAVY WATER (D_2O)			
	Units	H_2O	D_2O
Molecular mass		18.016	20.031
Boiling point	°C	100.00	101.431
Melting point	°C	0.000	3.813
Maximum density	$kg \cdot m^{-3}$	1 000.000	1 106.00
Temp. of maximum density	°C	3.98	11.185
Specific heat capacity at 3.98°C	$kJ \cdot (kg \cdot K)^{-1}$	4.205	4.30
Specific heat of vaporization at the boiling point	$kJ \cdot kg^{-1}$	2 256.416	2 320.0
Specific heat of fusion (melting)	$kJ \cdot kg^{-1}$	333.597	353.0

7

Where are we going?

In 1960, 10 per cent of the population of Essen, West Germany, had non-bacterial gastro-enteritis. The cause was believed to be the high concentration of salt and detergent in drinking water.

One of the aims of this booklet has been to make you more aware of the importance of water in the lives of all of us. The experiments should have helped you to understand how contaminants affect the environment.

Facing page 1 are drawings of several uses of water. In what ways can pollution affect these uses? Here are a few.

Ions will precipitate the stearate ion out of solution: for example, Fe^{2+} will affect soap's cleansing capabilities.

Nitrate ions and chloride ions can cause illness, if they are present in drinking water to excess.

Eutrophication kills fish and tends to encourage the growth of algae. This lessens the attractiveness of water for recreation and leisure.

Industrial pollutants kill algae and hence reduce oxygen production.

Finally, consider the possibility that *we* — not '*they*' — are responsible for pollution and its control. Politicians, advised by experts, draw up pollution legislation, but politicians are in office because we have voted for them. They have to listen to the wishes of the public when they tackle pollution problems. However, pollution control is not just a matter of spending large sums of money. The effects of laws on people have to be considered. For example, suppose that Company A is ordered to build a $10 million pollution control system. The cost of its products may have to go up. But this company's competitor in another country, Company B, is allowed to continue to pollute, thus keeping costs down. What might happen to the jobs of the employees of Company A?

Pollution knows no national or natural boundaries. We face it on all sides, and it is everybody's problem. What more can governments and individuals do to co-operate in the fight against this menace?

Figure 7-1. The choice is yours.

Word meanings

Aerobic   Depending for life on air (free oxygen).

Algae   Simple single-celled or many-celled rootless water-plants, containing chlorophyll.

Atomic fission   Splitting the nuclei of atoms, usually by firing slow neutrons at ^{235}U or ^{239}Pu, thereby releasing energy.

Bacteria   One-celled micro-organisms. (See coliform bacteria.)

Biochemical oxygen demand (B.O.D.)   Amount of dissolved oxygen required by organisms to decompose dead organic material in water; measured in parts per million.

Carbohydrates   Chemicals compounded only of carbon, hydrogen and oxygen. Examples: sugars, starches and cellulose.

Chlorination   Treatment of sewage and drinking water with chlorine to kill harmful bacteria.

Chlorophyll   Green-coloured materials in plants, essential for photosynthesis.

Coliform bacteria   While not in themselves harmful to humans, coliform bacteria indicate the possible presence of other faecal bacteria that *are* dangerous to health.

Condensation   Change of state from vapour to liquid.

Cooling water   Water used by industry for cooling, usually taken from a lake or river and returned there untreated.

Desalination   Removal of salts from water to make it drinkable.

Detergent   A substance, usually synthetic, that cleans in water, and will not form a scum in hard water.

Deuterium   D (^2_1H), is an isotope of hydrogen containing one proton and one neutron in the neucleus.

Dissolved oxygen   Amount of oxygen dissolved in water, usually about 10 ppm.

Ecology   Study of the relationships between species and their environment.

Ecosystem   A discrete system in which all material needs are provided from within itself.

Effluent   A liquid flowing away from a source, e.g. from a house, farm, sewage plant or industrial plant.

Emulsion   A dispersed suspension of one immiscible liquid in another.

Emulsifying agent   Substance that brings about an emulsion, e.g., soap with oil and water.

Eutrophication   The enrichment of a body of water with an excess of nutrients, usually nitrates and phosphates. This enrichment encourages the growth of algae.

Evaporation   The change of state from liquid to vapour; the opposite of condensation.

Fertilizer   Substance added to the earth to provide nutrients for plant growth.

Fixed nitrogen   Nitrogen combined with another chemical.

Flocculation   Process by which solids suspended in water are coagulated so that they may be filtered.

Fungi   Small plants that do not photosynthesize. They are decomposers.

Hard water   Water containing Ca^{2+}, Mg^{2+}, and Fe^{2+} ions, among others, will form a precipitate with the negative ion of soap.

Heavy water   Deuterium oxide, D_2O, used as a moderator in some atomic reactors.

Hydrogen bonding   The mutual attraction between hydrogen in one molecule and oxygen, nitrogen or fluorine in another molecule, as exemplified by H_2O, NH_3, HF.

Hydrologic cycle   The continuous path of a part of the world's water: evaporation of the liquid to vapour, condensation of the vapour into clouds; precipitation in the form of rain, dew, frost, snow, etc.; flow of the runoff into bodies of water; re-evaporation, and so on.

Hydrophilic	Water-loving.
Hydrophobic	Water-hating.
Industrial effluents	Waste products of industry, usually inorganic substances, discharged in water.
Minerals	Inorganic chemicals found on earth.
Moderator	Substance that slows down neutrons in a nuclear reactor.
Nuclear fission	See Atomic fission.
Permanently hard water	Water whose hardness cannot be destroyed by boiling, but can be destroyed by other methods.
Photosynthesis	The process by which green plants use chlorophyll and sunlight to convert carbon dioxide and water into carbohydrates and oxygen.
Phytoplankton	Plant life, often microscopic, that floats and drifts on or near the surface of bodies of water.
Plankton	Plant or animal life, often microscopic, which floats and drifts on or near the surface of bodies of water.
Pollution	Any additions to an ecological system that harm it and disrupt its natural balance.
Precipitate	An insoluble substance formed from the reaction of two soluble substances.
Primary sewage treatment	First stage of sewage treatment, which screens out large solids and allows smaller ones to settle.
Protein	A compound of high molecular mass, composed of carbon, hydrogen, oxygen, nitrogen and sometimes sulfur, necessary for the growth and repair of living tissue.
Respiration	Oxidation of carbohydrates producing energy, carbon dioxide and water.
Secondary sewage treatment	Disgestion of nutrients by aerobic bacteria.
Sewage	Usually domestic and animal effluents, as distinct from industrial effluents.
Sludge	The material that settles from sewage in sewage treatment plants.
Soap	A salt of a fatty acid (for instance sodium stearate) that is neutral and produces a scum in hard water.
Soft water	Water that is free of the ions that cause hard water. Lathers easily with soap.
Temporarily hard water	Water whose hardness can be destroyed by boiling.
Tertiary sewage treatment	Removal of chemicals, usually phosphates and nitrates, that have escaped primary and secondary treatment.
Transpiration	Passing of water through the roots and stems of plants and voiding through the leaves.

Special materials for experiments

This list is of special materials not normally stocked in a school laboratory, but which would be needed for a class of thirty students to complete all the experiments in this book.

Chapter 2
edta solution (1 dm^3)
Eriochrome Black T (indicator)
Permutit (100 g)
Wanklyn's soap solution

Chapter 3
Manganese (II) sulphate 500 g)
Methylene blue (5 g)
Millipore filtration apparatus
Potassium iodide (200 g)

Chapter 5
Calcium hypochlorite

Chapter 6
Castor oil (250 cm^3)
1,4-dichlorobenzene (1 kg)

Reference materials

Books

Adamson, R.G. *Pollution: An Ecological Approach*. London: Heinemann Educational, 1972.

Alexander, P. *Atomic Radiation of Life*. Penguin, 1965.

Andrews, W.A. (Ed.) *Environmental Pollution*. Scarborough, Ont.: Prentice-Hall, 1972.

Andrews, W.A. (Ed.). *Freshwater Ecology*. Scarborough, Ont.: Prentice-Hall, 1972.

Behrman, A.S. *Water is Everybody's Business*. New York: Doubleday, 1972.

Bennet, M. *Intelligent Woman's Guide to Atomic Radiation*. Penguin, 1964.

Brinkhurst, D.O., Chant, D.A. *This Good, Good Earth*. Toronto: Macmillan, 1971.

Brubaker, S. *To Live on Earth*. Signet Mentor Books, 1972.

Chant, D.A. (Ed.). *Pollution Probe*. Toronto: New Press, 1970.

Davies, D. *Fresh Water*. New York: Natural History Press, 1969.

Dunn, D.L., Stevens, J.G.R. (Eds.), *Pesticides and Human Welfare*. O.U.P., 1976.

Furon, R. *Problem of Water: A World Study*. London: Faber and Faber, 1967.

Johnstone, A.H., Morrison, T.I. *Chemistry Takes Shape*. London: Heinemann Educational, 1967. (Books 3 and 4)

LAMP Project, Topic Brief 3, *Pollution*. A.S.E., 1976.

Leopold, L.B., Davis, K.S. *Water*. New York: Life, 1969.

Moore, E. *Detergents*. Unilever, Lever Detergents, 1969.

Munro, L. *Chemistry in Engineering*. Englewood Cliffs, N.J.: Prentice-Hall, 1964.

Oliver, H.P.H. *Water: Chemistry Background Book*. London: Longman, 1968. (Nuffield)

Schools Council Project Environment, *Ethics and Environment*. Longman, 1975.

Taylor, R.J. *Water*. Unilever, Lever Detergents, 1969.

Tucker, A. *The Toxic Metals*. New York: Ballentine, 1972.

Ward, B., Dubos, R. *Only One Earth*. Penguin, 1972.

Yapp, W.B. *Production, Pollution, Protection*. London: Wykeham, 1972.

Films

*Before It's Too Late (C.I.L.)
*Chemistry of Water (C.I.L.)
*Clean Water, It's Your Decision (M.O.E., Ont.) (Shell)
Detergents (Unilever)
+ Downstream (Inco)
Element 3 (N.F.B.)
Energy and Society (O.H.)
Hard Water (Unilever)
*The Invisible River (M.O.E., Ont.)
*Lake Odyssey (M.O.E., Ont.)
Life Between The Tides (NAVA)

*The Living Lakes (BP)
*The Living River (BP)
Load on Top (Shell)
One in a Million (N.F.L.)
Physics and Chemistry of Water (Unilever)
Planet Earth (BP)
*Planet Water (BP)
The River Must Live (Shell)
River with a Problem (N.F.B.)
Threat in the Water (Shell)
Torrey Canyon (Unilever)
*Waste Not, Want Not (O.H.)
ı Water (U.N.)
Water in Biology (Unilever)

Addresses

*available from
Modern Talking Picture Services
143 Sparks Avenue
Toronto, Ontario M2H 2S5

+ available from
Association Films
333 Adelaide St. W.
Toronto, Ontario M5V 1R6

ı National Film Board
P.O. Box 6100
Montreal, Qué. H3C 3H5

BP Film Library
15 Beaconsfield Rd.
London NW 10 2LE

National Film Library
75 Albert Street
Ottawa, Ontario K1P 5E6

NAVA
2 Paxton Place
Gypsy Road
London SE 27

Ontario Hydro
Energy Education Dept.
700 University Avenue
Toronto, Ontario M5G 1X6

Shell Film Library
505 University Avenue
Toronto, Ontario M5W 1E1

Shell Film Library
25 The Burroughs
Hendon
London NW 4 4AT

Unilever
P.O. Box 68
Unilever House
London EC 4P 4BQ

Table of some SI units

SI UNIT REFERENCE TABLE

	Name	Base units	Derived units	SI equivalents of obsolescent units
Length	kilometre		1 km	1.609 344 * km = 1 mile
	[1] metre	1 m		0.9144* m = 1 yd
				0.3048* m = 1 ft
	centimetre		1 cm	2.54* cm = 1 in
Area	square metre		1 m²	0.092 903 04* m² = 1 ft²
				0.836 127 36* m² = 1 yd²
	square hectometre (hectare)		1 hm² (1 ha)	0.404 685 642 241 ha = 1 acre
Volume	cubic metre		1 m³	0.764 554 857 984 m³ = 1 yd³
				0.028 316 846 592 0 m³ = 1 ft³
	cubic centimetre		1 cm³	16.387 064* cm³ = 1 in³
	cubic decimetre = (litre) = 1000 cm³		1 dm³ = (1 L or 1 l)	1.136 522 1 dm³ (L) = 1 qt
Mass	[2] kilogram	1 kg		0.453 592 37 kg = 1 lb (avdp.)
	gram		1 g	0.035 273 962 g = 1 oz (avdp.)
	[3] mole	1 mol		
Time	[4] second	1 s		1 s = 1 sec
Force	newton	(kg·m·s⁻²)	1 N	0.000 01* N = 1 dyne
				4.448 221 676 59 N = 1 lb
Pressure, stress	pascal	(N·m⁻²)	1 Pa	6 894.759 086 77 Pa = 1 lb·in⁻²
	megapascal		1 MPa	0.101 325 023 83 MPa = 1 atm.
Energy, work	joule	(N·m)	1 J	4.184 00 J = 1 cal. (thermochem.)
				0.000 000 1* J = 1 erg
	kilojoule		1 kJ	3 600.00* kJ = 1 kW·h
Power	watt	(J·s⁻¹)	1 W	0.292 8746 W = 1 BTU·h⁻¹
Temperature	[5] kelvin (=°C)	1 K		0.555 555 5 K = 1°F
Electric current	[6] ampere	1 A		
	milliampere		1 mA	
Luminous intensity	[7] candela	1 cd		

*exact

[1] The metre is now defined as 1 650 763.73 wavelengths in vacuum of the radiation corresponding to the transition between levels $2p_{10}$ and $5d_5$ at the orange-red line of the spectrum of the krypton-86 atom.

[2] The standard kilogram is still the mass of the cylinder of platinum-iridium alloy at the International Bureau of Weights and Measures, Sèvres, France.

[3] The mole is defined as the amount (mass) of any pure substance or system that contains the same number of molecules (or atoms, ions or electrons, as the case may be) as there are atoms in exactly 12 g of pure carbon-12 (the ^{12}C nuclide).

[4] The second is defined as the duration of 9 192 631 770 cycles, or periods, of the radiation corresponding to the transition between the two hyperfine energy levels of the ground state of the cesium-133 atom.

[5] The kelvin is defined as $\frac{1}{273.16}$ of the thermodynamic temperature of the triple point of water, pure air-free water at 0.01 $^{\circ}C$ (273.16 K) under vapour pressure of 610.483 26 Pa. The triple point of water is the temperature cum pressure at which ice, liquid water and water vapour are in equilibrium. Air-free water means water in a vacuum with no dissolved air in it. (0.00 K is absolute zero, the point where theoretically all molecular motion ceases. One kelvin is equivalent to one Celsius degree. Therefore, 0.00K $=-273.15\,^{\circ}C$.)

[6] The ampere is defined as the magnitude of electric current that, if maintained in two straight parallel conductors (wires) of negligible circular cross-section, of 'infinite' length, and placed 1 m apart in vacuum, would produce a magnetic-field force between the conductors of 0.2 μN per metre of length.

[7] The candela is defined as the perpendicular luminous intensity of a surface area $\frac{1}{600\ 000}$ m^2 (1.6 mm^2) of a fully radiating cavity (black body) at the temperature of freezing platinum (2042 K) under a pressure of 101.325 kPa.

Index